Recorded by PETER FRAMPTON on A&M Records

BABY, I LOVE YOUR WAY

Words and Music by
PETER FRAMPTON

Moderately

Sud-den-ly ___ the day ___ turns in-to night ___ far a-way ___ from the cit-y. ___
Won-der ___ how they have the power to shine ___ *(shine ___ shine)* ___ I can see them ___ un-der the pine, ___ but

Don't ___ hes-i-tate ___ 'cause your love ___ won't wait. ___

Chorus (3 times)

Ooh, Ba-by I Love Your Way.
Wan-na tell you I love your way.
Wan-na be with you night and day.

D.S. al Coda

I can see the

sun - set in your eyes___ brown and grey and blue be-sides, Clouds are stalk - ing is - lands in the sun,___ I wish I could buy one out of sea - son.

don't _____ hes-i-tate _____ 'cause your love _____ won't wait. _____

Chorus (4 times)

1. 4. Ooh, Ba-by I Love _____ Your Way. _____
2. Wan-na tell you I love _____ your way. _____
3. Wan-na be with you night _____ and day. _____

THIS ONE'S FOR YOU

Recorded by BARRY MANILOW on ARISTA Records

Lyrics by
MARTY PANZER

Music by
BARRY MANILOW

Slowly

1. This one-'ll nev-er sell,_ they'll nev-er un-der-stand,_
2. I've done a hun-dred songs,_ from fan-ta-sies_ to lies,_
%. I've got it all,_ it seems,_ for all it means_ to me,_

I don't e-ven sing_ it well,_ I try, but I_ just can't._ But I
But this one's so real_ for me_ that I'm the one_ who cries._ But I
But I sing of things_ I miss_ and things that used_ to be._ And I

Copyright © 1976 KAMAKAZI MUSIC CORP. c/o Miles J. Lourie, 250 West 57th Street, New York, New York 10019
International Copyright Secured   Made in U.S.A.   All Rights Reserved
Used by permission

sing it ev-'ry night, and I fight to keep it in, 'Cause
sing it ev-'ry **night,** and I fight to hide the tears, 'Cause
won-der ev-'ry night if you might just miss me too, And

This One's For You, This One's For
This One's For You, This One's For
I sing for you, I sing for

1. You.
2. You.

This One's For You wher-ev-er you are, To
This One's For You wher-ev-er I go, To

say that noth-ing's been the same since we've been a-part.
say the things I should have said, things that you should know.

This one's for all the love we once knew,

Like ev-ery-thing else I have, This One's For You, oh.

D.S. to 2nd ending al Coda

Coda

This one's to say____ that all I can do____ is hope that you____ will hear___ me sing___ 'cause This One's For You.____ Oh,_____

Fade out

This One's For You____ wher-ev-er you are_____ To say that noth-ing's been____ the same_____ since we've been___ a-part.___ Oh,_____

WEEKEND IN NEW ENGLAND

Recorded by BARRY MANILOW on ARISTA Records

Words and Music by
RANDY EDELMAN

Moderately

1. Last night I said good-bye, Now it seems years. I'm
2. Time in New England took me a-way to

back in the cit-y where noth-ing is clear. But
long rock-y beach-es and you by the bay. We

thoughts of me hold-ing you, bring-ing us near.
start-ed a sto-ry whose end must now wait.

And tell me,

poco rit.

Copyright © 1975, 1976 UNART MUSIC CORPORATION/PIANO PICKER MUSIC
All rights administered by UNART MUSIC CORPORATION, New York, N.Y.

International Copyright Secured   Made in U.S.A.   All Rights Reserved
Used by permission

Chorus

When will our eyes meet? When can I touch you? When will this strong yearning end? And when will I hold you a-gain.

gain. I feel the change com-in', I feel the wind blow. I feel brave and dar-ing, I feel my blood flow. With you I could bring out all the love that I have. With you there's a heav-en, So earth ain't so bad.

And tell me,

When will our eyes meet? When can I touch you? When will this strong yearn-ing end? And when will I hold you a-gain, a-gain.

Recorded by JIM CROCE on ABC Records

BAD, BAD LEROY BROWN

Words and Music by
JIM CROCE

Moderate boogie-rock tempo

G   A7

1. Well, the South-side of Chi-ca-go is the bad-dest part of town.
2. (Now Le-)roy he a gam-bler and he like his fan-cy clothes.
3. (Well, Fri-)day 'bout a week a-go, Le-roy shoot-in' dice

B7   C

And if you go down there you bet-ter just be-ware of a
And he like to wave his dia-mond rings in front of
And at the edge of the bar sat a girl name of Do-ris And

D7   G

man name of Le-roy Brown. Now Le-roy more than trou-ble, you see he
ev-'ry-bod-y's nose. He got a cus-tom Con-ti-nen-tal, he got a
oh, that girl looked nice. Well, he cast his eyes up-on her, and the

2650

Copyright © 1972, 1973 BLENDINGWELL MUSIC, INC.
Copyright © 1972, 1973 in U.S.A. and Canada BLENDINGWELL MUSIC, INC. and
AMERICAN BROADCASTING MUSIC, INC., c/o PUBLISHERS' LICENSING CORPORATION,
488 Madison Avenue, New York, N.Y.

International Copyright Secured   Made in U.S.A.   All Rights Reserved
Used by permission

stand 'bout six-foot-four; All the down-town la- dies call him
El- do- ra- do, too; He got a thir-ty- two gun in his
trou- ble soon be- gan, And Le- roy Brown, he learned a

"tree- top lov- er," al! the men just call him, "Sir."
pock- et for fun, he got a ra- zor in his shoe.
les- son 'bout mess- in' with the wife of a jeal- ous man.

And he's bad,

Chorus:

bad Le- roy Brown, the bad- dest man in the whole damned town; bad- er than old King Kong and

D C To Coda 1.,2. G Tacet 3. G Tacet
mean-er than a junk-yard dog. 2. Now Le- 3. Well, Fri- Well, the two
G A7
men took to fight-in', and when they pulled them from the floor
B7 C D7 G D.S. al Coda
Le-roy looked like a jig-saw puz-zle with a cou-ple of piec-es gone. And he's bad,
Coda G Tacet B7 C D C G
Yes, you were bad-der than old King Kong, and mean-er than a junk-yard dog.

BOHEMIAN RHAPSODY

Recorded by QUEEN on ELEKTRA Records

Words and Music by
FREDDIE MERCURY

Is this the real life? Is this just fan-ta-sy? Caught in a land-slide, No es-cape from re-al-i-ty. O-pen your eyes,— Look up to the skies— and see, I'm just a poor boy, I need no sym-pa-thy, Be-cause I'm eas-y come, eas-y go, Lit-tle high, lit-tle low, An-y way the wind blows does-n't real-ly mat-ter to me, to— me.

Copyright © 1975 by B. FELDMAN AND CO., LTD., trading as TRIDENT MUSIC
138-140 Charing Cross Road, London WC2H 0ld, England
Distributed exclusively in the U.S.A. and Canada by THE BIG 3 MUSIC CORPORATION
International Copyright Secured   Made in U.S.A.   All Rights Reserved
Used by permission

Bb Gm Cm
1. Ma - ma just killed a man, Put a gun a-gainst his head, pulled my
2. Too late, my time has come, Sends shiv - ers down my spine, bod - y's
mf
F Bb Gm
trig - ger, now he's dead. Ma - ma, life had just be - gun, But
ach - ing all the time. Good-bye, ev-'ry - bod - y, I've got to go, Got-ta
Cm7 B+ Eb (Bb bass) F (A bass) Fm (Ab bass) Eb Bb (D bass) Cm
now I've gone and thrown it all a - way. Ma - ma, ooh, Did-n't
leave you all be - hind and face the truth Ma - ma, ooh,
Fm Bb 1. Eb Bb (D bass)
mean to make you cry, If I'm not back a - gain this time to - mor - row, car - ry on, car - ry
I don't want to die, I some-times wish I'd nev - er been born at
Cm Abm 4 fr. Eb Ab 4 fr. Fm7 2. Eb Bb (D bass)
on as if noth - ing real - ly mat - ters. all.

Cm
Fm
Db
Db (Cb bass)
Bbm
L'istesso tempo (♪ = ♩)
A
D
Adim
I see a lit - tle sil - hou - et - to of a man, Scar - a - mouche, Scar - a - mouche, will you
Db (Ab bass)
Ab
4 fr.
C (G bass)
E
do the Fan - dan - go.
Chorus:
Thun - der - bolt and light - ning, ver - y, ver - y fright - 'ning
f
No chord
me. (Gal - li - le - o.) Gal - li - le - o. (Gal - li - le - o.) Gal - li - le - o, Gal - li - le - o fig - a -
B
Bb
ro Mag - ni - fi - co.
(let ring)
Solo: I'm just a poor boy and no - bod - y loves me.
mf

Ab Eb Ebdim Eb Ab Eb Ebdim Eb Ab Eb (G bass)
4 fr.
Chorus:
He's just a poor boy from a poor fam - i - ly, Spare him his life from this
f
F Bb Ab Eb (G bass) F#dim Fm7 B Bb A Bb
mon - stros - i - ty.
mf
Solo:
Eas - y come, eas - y go,
B Bb A Bb Eb Bb Eb
will you let me go, Bis - mil - lah!
Chorus:
No, we will not let you go. (Let him go! ___
___) Bis - mil - lah! We will not let you go. (Let him go! ___) Bis - mil - lah! We
will not let you go. (Let me go.) Will not let you go. (Let me go.) Will not let you go. (Let me go. ___

Ah. No, no, no, no, no, no, no. (Oh ma-ma mi-a, ma-ma mi-a.) Ma-ma mi-a, let me go. Be-el-ze-bub has a dev-il put a-side for me, for me, for me. So you think you can stone me and spit in my eye. So you think you can

Bb Eb Ab 4 fr. Fm Bb
love me and leave me to die. Oh, baby,
Fm Bb Fm7 Bb Fm7 Bb
can't do this to me, baby, Just got-ta get out, just got-ta get right out-ta
Eb Cm Gm Cm Gm
here. Noth-ing real-ly mat-ters, An-y-one can see,
Cm Abm 4 fr. Bb11 Eb Ab (Eb bass) Eb Ebdim
Noth-ing real-ly mat-ters, Noth-ing real-ly mat-ters to me.
ritard.
a tempo
Bb (D bass) Bbm (Db bass) C7 C7-9 C7 F Bb F Abdim Gm7 F
poco a poco ritard. e dim.
An-y way the wind blows.
p

AT SEVENTEEN

Recorded by JANIS IAN on COLUMBIA Records

Words and Music by
JANIS IAN

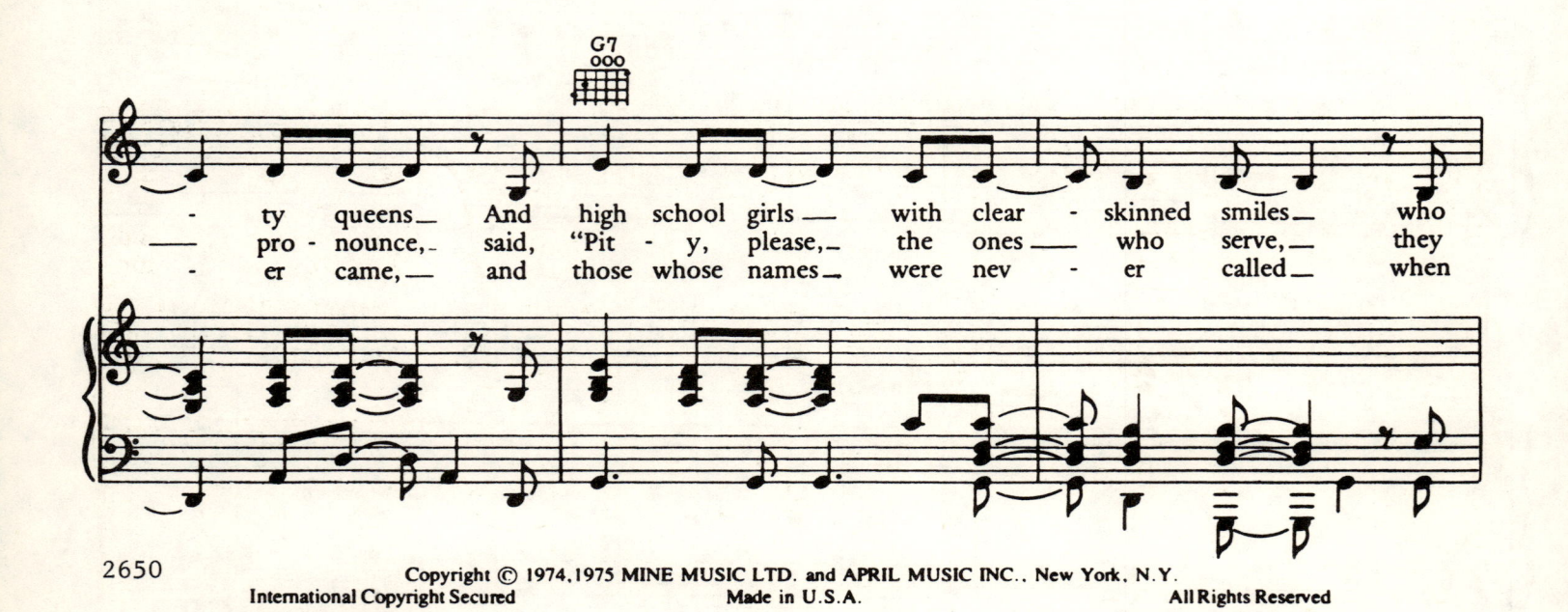

Moderately

I learned the truth at sev - en - teen____ that love was meant for beau -
(A) brown - eyed girl in hand - me downs____ whose name I nev - er could
(To) those of us who know____ the pain____ of val - en - tines that nev -

- ty queens____ And high school girls____ with clear - skinned smiles____ who
____ pro - nounce,____ said, "Pit - y, please,____ the ones____ who serve,____ they
- er came,____ and those whose names____ were nev - er called____ when

Copyright © 1974, 1975 MINE MUSIC LTD. and APRIL MUSIC INC., New York, N.Y.
International Copyright Secured   Made in U.S.A.   All Rights Reserved
Used by permission

mar - ried young and then re - tired. The
on - ly get what they de - serve. The
choos - ing sides for bas - ket - ball. It was

val - en - tines I nev - er knew, the Fri - day night cha - rades
rich re - la - tioned home - town queen mar - ries in - to what
long a - go and far a - way. The world was young - er than

of youth were spent on one more beau - ti - ful At
she needs A guar - an - tee of com - pa - ny And
to - day and dreams were all they gave for free to

sev - en - teen, I learned the truth. And
ha - ven for the eld - er - ly. Re -
ug - ly duck - ling girls like me. We all

those of us with rav - aged fac - es, lack - ing in the so -
mem - ber those who win the game lose the love they sought
play the game and when we dare to cheat our - selves at sol -

- cial grac - es, Des - p'rate - ly re - mained at home in -
- to gain In de - ben - tures of qual - i - ty and
- i - taire In - vent - ing lov - ers on the phone, re -

vent-ing lov-ers on the phone. Who called to say, "Come dance
du-bi-ous in-teg-ri-ty. Their small town eyes will gape
pent-ing oth-er lives un-known, that call and say, "Come dance

with me," and mur-mured vague ob-scen-i-ties.
at you in dull sur-prise when pay-ment due
with me" and mur-mur vague ob-scen-i-ties

It is-n't all it seems at sev-en-teen.
ex-ceeds ac-counts re-ceived at sev-en-teen.
at ug-ly girls like me at sev-en-teen.

2. A
3. To

BEFORE THE NEXT TEARDROP FALLS

Recorded by FREDDY FENDER on ABC/DOT Records

Words and Music by
BEN PETERS
VIVIAN KEITH

Moderately slow

If he brings you hap-pi-ness then I wish you both the best, it's your
hurts to let you go, dar-ling I want you to know that I'll

hap-pi-ness that mat-ters most of all. But if he
stand by you if ev-er you should call. And if

ev-er breaks your heart, if the tear-drops ev-er
I should ev-er hear that he made you shed a
ev-er leaves you blue, just re-mem-ber I love

start,
tear,   I'll be there Be-fore The Next Tear-drop
you,

To Coda

Copyright © 1967, 1968 FINGERLAKE MUSIC, INC., 3106 Belmont Blvd., Nashville, Tennessee
Assigned 1968 to SHELBY SINGLETON MUSIC, INC.

International Copyright Secured   Made in U.S.A.   All Rights Reserved
Used by permission

1. F Bb C7
Falls. Tho' it
2. F Bb F F7
Falls. I'll be
Bb C7 F
there an - y time you need me by your side To
G7 C7
dry a - way ev - 'ry tear - drop that you cried. If he
D.S. al Coda
Coda
F Bb F
Falls. Yes, I'll be there Be - fore The
C7 F Bb F
Next Tear - drop Falls.

FERNANDO

Recorded by ABBA on ATLANTIC Records

Words and Music by
BENNY ANDERSSON
STIG ANDERSON
BJORN ULVAEUS

Moderate

Can you hear the drums Fer-nan-do?
They were clos-er now Fer-nan-do.
Now we're old and grey Fer-nan-do.

I re-mem-ber long a-go an-oth-er star-ry night like
Ev-'ry ho-ur, ev-'ry min-ute seemed to last e-ter-nal-
and since man-y years I have-n't seen a ri-fle in your

this.
ly.
hand.

In the fi-re-light Fer-nan-do,
I was so a-fraid Fer-nan-do,
Can you hear the drums Fer-nan-do?

Copyright © 1975 by UNION SONGS AB, Stockholm, Sweden for the world
This arrangement Copyright © 1976 by ARTWORK MUSIC CO., INC., for the U.S.A. and Canada
Sole Selling Agent: IVAN MOGULL MUSIC CORPORATION, 40 East 49th Street, New York, N.Y. 10017
International Copyright Secured   Made in U.S.A.   All Rights Reserved
Used by permission

you were hum-ming to your-self and soft-ly strum-ming your gui-
we were young and full of life and none of us pre-pared to
Do you still re-call the fright-ful night we crossed the Ri - o

tar.   I could hear the dis-tant drums and sounds of bu - gle calls were
die.   And I'm not ash-amed to say the roar of guns and can - nons
Grande? I can see it in your eyes how proud you were to fight for

1. com-ing from a - far.
2.3. al-most made me cry.
freedom in this land.

There was some-thing in the air that night,_ the stars_ were bright,_ Fer-nan-do. They were shin-ing there for you and me,_ for li-ber-ty, Fer-nan-do. Though we nev-er thought that we could lose,_ there's no re-gret._ If I had to do the same a-gain,___ I would ___ my friend, ___ Fer-nan- do.

If I had to do the same a-gain, ___ I would ___ my friend, ___ Fer-nan- do.

There was some-thing in the air that night, ___ the stars ___

D.C. al Coda

Coda

A
were bright, Fer-nan- do. They were shin-ing there for
E7
A
Gdim
you and me, for li- ber-ty, Fer-nan- do. Though we nev-er thought that we could lose,
F♯
B7
there's no re-gret.
If I had to do the
E7
A
Repeat and Fade
same a-gain, I would my friend, Fer-nan- do. If I had to do the

AND I LOVE YOU SO

Recorded by PERRY COMO on RCA Records

Words and Music by
DON McLEAN

Moderately slow

1.-3. And I love you so,
2. And you love me too,

The peo-ple ask me how, How I've lived till now,
Your thoughts are just for me, You set my spir-it free,

I tell them I don't know. I guess they un-der-stand,
I'm hap-py that you do. The book of life is brief,

Copyright © 1970, 1972 MAYDAY MUSIC, INC. and YAHWEH TUNES, INC.
International Copyright Secured   Made in U.S.A.   All Rights Reserved
Used by permission

36

How lonely life has been, / *But life began again,*
And once a page is read, / *All but love is dead,*
The day you took my hand. / *That is my belief.*
And, yes, I know how lonely life can be, (love - less) The shadows follow me and the night won't set me free. But I don't

Dm7
let the eve - ning get me down,
(bring)
Now___ that you're a -
G7
G7-9
1. C
C6
C
C6
2. C
C6
C
C6
D. S. al Coda
round me.___
me.___
Coda
F
G7
C
I tell them___ I don't know.___
Tacet
rit.

HELP ME MAKE IT THROUGH THE NIGHT

Recorded by KRIS KRISTOFFERSON on MONUMENT Records

Words and Music by
KRIS KRISTOFFERSON

Take the rib - bon from your hair, Shake it loose and let it fall,
Come and lay down by my side Till the early mornin' light.
Yes - ter - day is dead and gone And to - morrow's out of sight,

Lay - in' soft up - on my skin, Like the shad - ows on the wall.
All I'm tak - in' is your time.
And it's sad to be a - lone. *(To Fine)*

Copyright © 1970 by COMBINE MUSIC CORPORATION, 35 Music Square East, Nashville, Tennessee 37203
International Copyright Secured   Made in U.S.A.   All Rights Reserved
Used by permission

2.
D
G
To next strain
Help me make it thru the night.
Fine
D
G
D
Help me make it thru the night.
D
G
I don't care who's right or wrong,
I don't
D
try to un - der - stand.
Let the dev - il take to -
E7
A7
D.S. al Fine
mor - row.
Lord, to - night I need a friend.

FOREVER LOVERS

Recorded by MAC DAVIS on COLUMBIA Records

Words and Music by
STERLING WHIPPLE

For - ev - er lov - ers,_____ For - ev - er friends. A life-time's a short time_____ When love nev - er ends.

1. They checked in - to a small ho - tel; she blushed when he asked for the brid - al suite.
2. (She) climbed in - to the bed; he snapped his fin - gers. Said, "I've got to get cham - pagne.
3. (She) checks in - to the old ho - tel and pays a lit - tle ex - tra for the suite.

Copyright © 1976 TREE PUBLISHING CO., INC., 8 Music Square West, Nashville, Tennessee 37203
International Copyright Secured   Made in U.S.A.   All Rights Reserved
Used by permission

| Bb | F | | Bb | Am |

'Twas the be-gin-ning of their lives to-geth-er, An-xious-ly they'd wait-ed for the
There's a lit-tle store right down the block, I'll on-ly be a min-ute. Close your
She slips in-to the fad-ed neg-li-gée and brush-es down her hair of

| Gm | Gm7 | C | | Eb |

mo-ment that their love could be com-plete. She reached in-side her brand new trav-'lin'
eyes and, hon, I'll be right back a-gain." And time goes by so slow-ly she's not
gray, and lays her bod-y down to wait. And the night air through the cur-tains makes a

| Bb | | F | Eb | Bb |

bag and found her brand new neg-li-gée, and then she shy-ly slipped it on.
sure how much has passed,— but she hears the si-ren scream-in' through the night.
sound like some-one breath-in', And she reach-es for him with her fin-ger-tips.

And sud-den-ly, he re-al-ized the beau-ty of the ten-der prize he'd
And sev-en hours later, they find her rock-in' on the bed, just
And they find her in the morn-in' with tear stains on her pil-low, and a

wait-ed for so long and fi-n'ly won.
sing-in' in the ear-ly morn-in' light.
smile like a kiss up-on her lips.

2. She

For-ev-er lov-ers, For-ev-er friends. A life-time's a

short time___ when love nev-er ends. 3. She

Coda
For-ev-er lov-ers,___ For-ev-er friends.

A life-time's a short-time,___ I knew I'd see you a-gain.

For-ev-er when love nev-er ends.

EVIL WOMAN

Recorded by ELECTRIC LIGHT ORCHESTRA on UNITED ARTISTS Records

Words and Music by
JEFF LYNNE

You made a fool of me___ but them bro-ken dreams___ have got to end.___

1. Hey wom-an,___ you got the blues 'Cause you ain't got no___ one else___ to use, There's an o-pen road___ that leads___ no-where,___ so just

Copyright © 1975 UNART MUSIC CORPORATION and JET MUSIC INCORPORATED
All rights administered by UNART MUSIC CORPORATION, New York, N.Y.
International Copyright Secured Made in U.S.A. All Rights Reserved
Used by permission

make some miles ____ be-tween here and there. There's a hole in my head ___ where the rain __ comes in, You took my bod-y and played ___ to win, Ha, ha wom-an it's a cry-in' shame, But you ain't got no-bod-y else ___ to blame.

Chorus
Am Em7 Dm7 Em7 Am Em7 Dm7 Em7
E - vil wom - an, E - vil wom - an
mf
Am Em7 Dm7 Em7 Am Em7 Dm Em7
To Coda
E - vil wom - an. E - vil wom - an.
Verse
Am Em7 Dm7 Em7 Am Em7
2. Rolled in from an - oth - er town, Hit some gold too hard to set -
mp
Dm7 Em7 Am Em7 Dm7 Em7
tle down, But a fool and his mon - ey soon go sep -'rate ways, And

Am
Em7
Dm7
Em7
you found a fool ly - in' in a daze.
Am
Em7
Dm7
Em7
Am
Em7
Ha ha wom - an what you gon - na do,
You des - troyed all the vir - tues that the
Dm7
Em7
Am
Em7
Dm7
Em7
Lord gave you,
It's so good that you're feel - in' pain
But you
Fmaj7
G
C
D.S. al Coda
bet - ter get your face on board the ver - y next train.
f

3. E-vil wom-an how you done me wrong, But now you're try-in' to wail a dif-f'rent song,
Ha ha fun-ny how you broke me up, you made the wine now you drink a cup.
I came run-nin' ev-'ry time you cried, Thought I saw love smil-in' in your eyes,
Ha ha___ ver-y nice to know that you ain't got no_ place left_ to go.___

D.S. and fade

Recorded by MORRIS ALBERT on RCA Records

FEELINGS
(¿Dime?)

Ballad

Spanish Lyrics by
THOMAS FUNDORA

English Words and Music by
MORRIS ALBERT

2650

Em (D# Bass)
Em7 (D Bass)
A7
rolling down on my face, trying to for-
brotan de mis ojos trato de olvi-
Am
D7
G
get my feelings of love.
dar mis sufrimientos de amor.
E7
C
Am7
D7
Feelings, for all my life I'll
¿Dime? si siempre yo a-
Bm
E7
Am
feel it. I wish I've never met you, girl;
sí te amé ¿Porque ahora sé lo tonto que fuí?
sim.

you'll nev-er come a - gain.
Ja - más tú vol - ve - rás.

Feel - ings, wo wo wo, feel - ings, wo wo wo,
¿Di - me? Wo wo wo, ¿Di - me? Wo wo wo

feel you a - gain in my arms.
¿Di - me? A - quí en mis bra - zos.

Feel - ings, ____ feel - ings like I've
¿Di - me?____ Es que

Em7
(D Bass)
A7
nev - er lost you, and feel - ings like I'll
pien - so que ya te he per - di - do, y pre - sien - to que sin
Am
D7
G
nev - 3 er have you a - gain in my heart. life.
tí mi vi - da no, no tie - ne. ra - zón.
E7+5
E7
To Coda
C
Am7
D7
Feel - ings, for all my life I'll
¿Di - me? si siem - pre yo a -
Bm
E7
Am
feel it. I wish I've nev - er met you, girl:
sí te a - mé ¿Por-que a-ho - ra sé lo ton - to que fuí?

you'll nev - er come a - gain.
Ja - más tu vol - ve - rás.

Feel - ings, wo wo wo
¿Di - me? Wo wo wo

feel - ings, wo wo wo, feel - ings
¿Di - me? Wo wo wo ¿Di - me?

a - gain in my arms.
A - quí en mis bra - zos.

repeat and fade

DELTA DAWN

Recorded by HELEN REDDY on CAPITOL Records

Words and Music by
ALEX HARVEY
LARRY COLLINS

Slowly, with a beat

Chorus

Del-ta Dawn, what's that flow-er you have on? Could it be a fad-ed rose from days gone by? And did I hear you say he was a meet-in' you here to-day to take you to his man-sion in the sky. 1. She's sky.

To next strain / *Fine*

Copyright © 1972 UNITED ARTISTS MUSIC CO., INC. and BIG AX MUSIC
All rights administered by UNITED ARTISTS MUSIC CO., INC., New York, N.Y.
International Copyright Secured Made in U.S.A. All Rights Reserved
Used by permission

Verse

for-ty-one and her dad-dy still calls her ba-by,
young-er days they called her Del-ta Dawn,

All the folks a-round Browns-ville say she's cra-zy, 'Cause she
Pret-ti-est wom-an you ev-er laid eyes on, Then a

walks down-town with a suit-case in her hand,
man of low de-gree stood by her side, And

1. *Look-in' for a mys-te-rious dark-haired man.* 2. In her
2. *prom-ised her he'd take her for his bride.*

D.S. al Fine

COUNTRY ROAD

Recorded by JAMES TAYLOR on WARNER BROS. Records

Words and Music by
JAMES TAYLOR

Slowly

Take____ to the high-way won't you lend me____ your name____

Your way____ and my way seem to be one and the same,

Ma-ma don't un-der-stand it___ she wants to know where I've been. I'd have to be some___ kind of nat-ural born fool to want to pass that way a-gain.___ But you know I could feel it___
(2nd time) But I could be there, Lord.___ On a coun-try road___

Sail on home to Jesus won't you good girls and boys?

I'm all in pieces you can have your own choice But

I can see a Heavenly band. Full of angels coming to set me free. I

don't know nothing 'bout the why or when, but I can tell you that it's bound to be because I could feel it / on a coun-try road.

I guess my feet know where they want me to go walk-ing on a coun-try road.

D.S. al Coda

Coda
D
C
(D Bass)
Walk on down, walk on down, walk on down, walk on down, walk-ing on a coun-try road.
D
No chord
La la la la la la la la la la la la
D
C
G
la la la la la la la la la la la la la Coun-try road
D
C
G
Walk-ing on a coun-try road.
D
C
G
Repeat and fade
Coun-try road

Recorded by WILLIE NELSON on RCA Records

FIRE AND RAIN

Words and Music by
JAMES TAYLOR

Slowly

Verses 1 & 2:

Just yes-ter-day morn-ing they let me know____ you were gone____
Look down up-on me, Je-sus, you've got to help me make a stand____

Su-san the plans they made put an end to you
You've just got to see me through an-oth-er day

I walked out this morn-ing and I wrote down this song____
My bod-y's ach-ing and my time is at hand____

Copyright © 1969, 1970 by BLACKWOOD MUSIC INC. and COUNTRY ROAD MUSIC, INC.
All rights administered by BLACKWOOD MUSIC INC., 51 West 52nd Street, New York, New York
International Copyright Secured   Made in U.S.A.   All Rights Reserved
Used by permission

I just can't re-mem-ber who to send it to.
And I won't make it an-y oth-er way.

Chorus:
I've seen fire and I've seen rain I've seen
sun-ny days that I thought would nev-er end I've seen
lone-ly times when I could not find a friend But I
al-ways thought that I'd see you a-gain.

1., 2.
C9
2nd time to Verse 3

2. Won't you
3. Now I'm

Fine
C9

Fine

Verse 3:

C — Gm7/C — F/C — C
walk-ing my mind to an eas-y time my back turned towards the sun

C — G/C — B♭/C
Lord knows when the cold wind blows it-'ll turn your head a-round Well, there's

C — Gm7/C — F/C — C
hours of time on the tel-e-phone line to talk a-bout things to come

C — G/C — B♭/C
Sweet dreams and fly-ing ma-chines in pie-ces on the ground.

D.S. al Fine

2650

CAROLINA IN THE PINES

Recorded by MICHAEL MURPHEY on EPIC Records

Words and Music by
MICHAEL MURPHEY

Moderately (not slow)

1. She came to me, said she knew me, said she'd known me a long time. And she
2. (There's a) new moon on the four-teenth ___ first quar-ter, the twen-ty - first, And a
3. (When the) frost shows on the win-dows and the wood-stove smokes and glows, As the

spoke of be-ing in love with ev-'ry moun-tain she had climbed. And she
full moon on the last week ___ brings a full-ness to the earth. There's no
fire grows we can warm our souls ___ watch-in' rain-bows in the coals. And we'll

Copyright © 1975 by MYSTERY MUSIC, INC.
All rights administered by BLACKWOOD MUSIC INC., 51 West 52nd Street, New York, N.Y.
International Copyright Secured   Made in U.S.A.   All Rights Reserved
Used by permission

talked of trails she walked up far a-bove the tim-ber-line. From that
guess work in the clock-work of the world's heart or___ mine.
talk of trails we've walked up far a-bove the tim-ber-line. There are

night on___ I knew I'd write songs___ with Car-o-li-na in the
nights I___ on-ly feel right___ with Car-o-li-na in the
nights I___ on-ly feel right___ with Car-o-li-na in the

pines.
pines.
pines.

2. There's a
3. When the

66

Recorded by MICHEL LEGRAND
ACADEMY AWARD WINNER
From the United Artists Motion Picture "THE THOMAS CROWN AFFAIR"

THE WINDMILLS OF YOUR MIND
(Theme From "The Thomas Crown Affair")

Lyric by
MARILYN and ALAN BERGMAN

Music by
MICHEL LEGRAND

Round like a cir-cle in a spi-ral, like a wheel with-in a wheel, Nev-er end-ing or be-gin-ning on an ev-er spin-ning reel, Like a snow-ball down a moun-tain, or a car-ni-val bal-loon, Like a car-ou-sel that's turn-ing run-ning rings a-round the

Mind! Like a tun-nel that you fol-low to a tun-nel of its own, Down a hol-low to a cav-ern where the sun has nev-er shone, Like a door that keeps re-volv-ing in a half for-got-ten dream, Or the rip-ples from a peb-ble some-one toss-es in a

2650

Copyright © 1968 UNITED ARTISTS MUSIC CO., INC., 729 Seventh Avenue, New York, N.Y. 10019
International Copyright Secured   Made in U.S.A.   All Rights Reserved
Used by permission

moon.
stream. } Like a clock whose hands are sweep-ing past the min-utes of its face, And the world is like an ap-ple whirl-ing si-lent-ly in space, Like the cir-cles that you find in The Wind-mills Of Your Mind! Keys that jin-gle in your pock-et, words that jan-gle in your head, Why did sum-mer go so quick-ly? Was it some-thing that you said? Lov-ers walk a-long a shore and leave their foot-prints in the sand. Is the sound of dis-tant drum-ming just the fin-gers of your hand? Pic-tures hang-ing in a

E7
Am
D7
hall-way and the frag-ment of a song, Half re-mem-bered names and fac-es, but to whom do they be-
Gmaj7
Cmaj7
F#m7-5
long? When you knew that it was o-ver you were sud-den-ly a-ware That the au-tumn leaves were
(Girl) When you knew that it was o-ver in the au-tumn of good-byes, For a mo-ment you could
poco a poco ritard.
B7
Em
turn-ing to the col-or of her hair!
not re-call the col-or of his eyes!
Like a cir-cle in a spi-ral, like a wheel with-in a
a tempo
B7
A#dim
wheel, Nev-er end-ing or be-gin-ning on an ev-er spin-ning reel, As the im-a-ges un-
Em
B7
Em
wind, Like the cir-cles that you find in The Wind-mills Of Your Mind!
poco a poco ritard.

Recorded by JIM CROCE on ABC Records

TIME IN A BOTTLE

Words and Music by
JIM CROCE

Moderately

If I could save time in a bot-tle_____ The first thing that
I could make days last for-ev-er,_____ If words could make

I'd like to do_____ Is to save ev-'ry day 'til e-
wish-es come true;_____ I'd save ev-'ry day like a

Copyright © 1971, 1972 BLENDINGWELL MUSIC, INC.
Copyright © 1971, 1972 in U.S.A. and Canada BLENDINGWELL MUSIC, INC. and
AMERICAN BROADCASTING MUSIC, INC.,
c/o PUBLISHERS' LICENSING CORPORATION, 488 Madison Avenue, New York, N.Y.

International Copyright Secured Made in U.S.A. All Rights Reserved
Used by permission

ter - ni - ty passes a - way Just to spend them with you.
treas - ure and then a - gain I would spend them with you.

If — But there nev - er seems to be e - nough time To do the things you want to do once you find them. I've looked a - round e - nough to know that you're the one I want to go thru time with.

A7 Dm Dm7# Dm7 Dm6
If I had a box just for wish - es And
Gm6 Gm A7 Gm7 A7 Dm6 A7 Dm A7 Dm
dreams that had nev - er come true; The box would be
Dm7 B♭ Gm7 Dm Gm
emp - ty ex - cept for the mem - 'ry of how they were an - swered by
A7 A7 Dm
D. S. al Coda
Coda
3 times
you. But there

YOUNG BLOOD

Recorded by BAD COMPANY on SWAN SONG Records

Words and Music by
JERRY LEIBER
MIKE STOLLER
DOC POMUS

Moderate Rock

I saw her stand-ing on the cor-ner,
I took one look and I was frac-tured,
I could-n't sleep that night for cry-in',

A yel-low rib-bon in her hair, I could-n't keep my-self from
I tried to walk and I was lame, I could-n't keep my-self from
I saw the ris-in' of the sun, And all night long my heart was

call-in', "Look-a there, look-a there, look-a there, look-a there!"
shout-in', "What's your name, what's your name, what's your name, what's your name?"
sigh-in', 'Cause she's the one, she's the one, she's the one, she's the one!"

Copyright © 1957 by TIGER MUSIC
BELINDA MUSIC, Publisher
UNICHAPPELL MUSIC, INC., sole-selling agent.
International Copyright Secured   Made in U.S.A.
ALL RIGHTS RESERVED including public performance for profit.
Any copying, arranging or adapting of this work without the consent of the owner is an infringement of copyright.
Used by permission

Bb
F
Young Blood, Young Blood,
mf
Bb
C7
To Coda
1.
Young Blood, I can't get you out of my mind.
2.
Bb
What cra - zy stuff, she looked so tough,
F
Bb
I had to fol - low her all the way home. Then things went bad

I met her Dad, He said, "You bet-ter leave my daugh-ter a-lone!"

D. S. al Coda

Coda

Young Blood,— Young Blood,—

Young Blood,— I can't get you out of my mind.

can't get you out of my mind.

LIVE AND LET DIE

Recorded by PAUL McCARTNEY & WINGS on UNITED ARTISTS Records

Words and Music by
PAUL McCARTNEY
LINDA McCARTNEY

Slowly

When you were young and your heart was an o-pen book,
(2nd time, instrumental till _____)

You used to say live and let live. (You know you did, you know you did, you know you did.) But if this ev-er-chang-ing world in which we live in makes you

Copyright © 1973 by UNITED ARTISTS MUSIC LTD., ATV MUSIC LTD. and McCARTNEY MUSIC LTD., London
All rights for the U.S.A. and Canada controlled by UNART MUSIC CORPORATION, New York, N.Y.
International Copyright Secured   Made in U.S.A.   All Rights Reserved
Used by permission

give it a cry,___ Say live and let die!___ Live and let die,___ Live and let die,___ Live and let die.___

What does it matter to ya,

when you got a job to do__ you got-ta do it well,__ You got-ta give the oth-er fel-low hell!__

D.C. al Coda

Coda

WEDDING BELL BLUES

Recorded by THE FIFTH DIMENSION on SOUL CITY Records

Moderately, with a beat

Words and Music by
LAURA NYRO

Bill, _____ I love you so. I al-ways will. I look at you and you see the pas-sion eyes of May. Oh, but am I ev-er gon-na see my wed-ding day? (Wed-ding day _____)

Bill, _____ I love you so. I al-ways will. And in your voice I hear a choir of car-ou-sels. Oh, but am I ev-er gon-na hear my wed-ding bells? (Wed-ding bells _____)

Copyright © 1966 by TUNA FISH MUSIC INC.
All rights administered by BLACKWOOD MUSIC INC., 51 West 52nd Street, New York, N.Y. 10019

Oh, I was on your side, Bill, when you were los - in'.
I was the one came run - nin', when you were lone - ly.

I'd nev-er scheme or lie, Bill, there's been no fool -
I have-n't lived one day, not lov-in' you on -

in'. But kiss-es and love won't car-ry me till you mar-ry me.
ly. But kiss-es and love won't car-ry me till you mar-ry me.

Bill, I love you so, I al-ways will. And though devo-tion rules my heart, I take no bows. Oh, but Bill, you

know I wan-na take my wed-ding vows. *(Wed-ding vows)* Come on, Bill.

(Come on, Bill.) So come on, Bill. *(Come on, Bill.)* I got the Wed-ding Bell Blues!

Fade out

Bill! I love you so, I al-ways will, I got the Wed-ding Bell Blues!

Recorded by STAMPEDERS on QUALITY Records

HIT THE ROAD JACK

Words and Music by
PERCY MAYFIELD

Cm Ab7 G7 Cm
mean - est old wom - an that I've ev - er seen. I guess if you said
Ab 4 fr. G7+5 Cm
so I'd have to pack my things and go. (That's right)
G7 Cm Ab7 G7+5 Cm Ab7 G7
Hit the road Jack and don't you come back no more, no more, no more, no more. Hit the
mf
Cm Ab7 G7 To Coda Cm Ab7 G7
road Jack and don't you come back no more. Now

ba-by, lis-ten ba-by, don't-a treat me this-a way— For I'll be back on my feet some day. Don't care if you do 'cause it's un-der-stood— you ain't got no mon-ey you just ain't no good.— Well, I guess if— you say so———— I'd have to pack my things— and go. (That's right) Hit the more. Don't you come back no more.

84

Recorded by BOBBY GOLDSBORO on UNITED ARTISTS Records

HONEY

Words and Music by
BOBBY RUSSELL

Moderately

See the tree, how big it's grown, but friend, it has-n't been too long, it was-n't big. I
She was al-ways young at heart,— kind-a dumb and kind-a smart and I loved her so.

laughed at her and she got mad, the first day that she plant-ed it was just a twig.
I sur-prised her with a pup-py, kept me up all Christ-mas eve, two years a-go. And

Then the first snow came and she ran out to brush the snow a-way— so it would-n't die, Came
it would sure em-bar-rass her when I came home from work-ing late—'cause I would know That

2650

Copyright © 1968 BIBO MUSIC PUBLISHERS, INC. (a division of T. B. HARMS COMPANY),
100 Wilshire Blvd., Suite 700, Santa Monica, California 90401

International Copyright Secured   All rights reserved including public performance for profit   Made in U.S.A.
Any copying, including photocopying, arranging or adapting of this work without the consent of the owner is an infringement of copyright
Used by permission

run-nin' in___ all ex-cit-ed, slipped and al-most hurt her-self, I laughed 'til I cried.___
she'd been sit-tin' there and cry-in' ov-er some sad and sil-ly

late, late show. And Hon-ey, I miss you___ and I'm be-ing

good___ And I'd love to be with you;___ if on-ly I

could. She wrecked the car and she was sad, and so a-fraid that I'd be mad, but
Yes, one day, while I was-n't home, while she was there and all a-lone, the

what the heck. Though I pre-tend-ed hard to be, guess you could say she saw through me and
An-gels came. Now all I have is mem-o-ries of Hon-ey, and I wake up nights and

hugged my neck. I came home un-ex-pect-ed-ly and found her cry-ing need-less-ly in the
call her name. Now my life's an emp-ty stage, where Hon-ey lived, and Hon-ey played, and

mid-dle of the day, And it was in the ear-ly Spring, when flow-ers bloom and Rob-ins sing, she
love grew up. A small cloud pas-ses ov-er head and cries down in the flow-er bed that

1. went a-way.
2. and Hon-ey, I Hon-ey loved. And

D.S. taking 1st line of lyrics and fade-out

Recorded by GLEN CAMPBELL on CAPITOL Records

COUNTRY BOY
(You Got Your Feet In L.A.)

Words and Music by
DENNIS LAMBERT
BRIAN POTTER

Moderate

Liv-in' in the ci-ty ain't nev-er been my i-dea of get-tin' it on.
Talk-in' on the te-le-phone, set-tin' up an-o-ther day of peo-ple to meet.

But the job de-mands that you make new plans be-
You got-ta do what's right, you got-ta spend the night,

fore your big chance is gone. You get a
stay-in' in touch with the street. When you're sur-

2650   Copyright © 1975 by ABC/DUNHILL MUSIC, INC. and ONE OF A KIND MUSIC, INC., Los Angeles, California
International Copyright Secured   Made in U.S.A.   All Rights Reserved
Used by permission

house in the hills, you're payin' ev-'ry-one's bills, and they tell ya that you're gon-na go far.
round-ed by friends, they say the fun nev-er ends, but I guess I'll nev-er fig-ure it out.

But in the back of my mind, I hear it time af-ter time: Is
'Cause in the back of my mind, I hear it time af-ter time: Is

that who you real-ly are?
this what it's all a-bout?
Coun-try boy, you got your

feet in L. A., but your mind's on Ten-nes-see. Look-in' back

I can re-mem-ber a time when I sang my songs for free. Coun-try boy, you got your feet in L. A.; take a look at ev-'ry-thing you own. But now and then my heart keeps go-ing home.

Coun-try

I CAN SEE CLEARLY NOW

Recorded by JOHNNY NASH on EPIC Records

Words and Music by
JOHNNY NASH

Moderato. (with a strong beat.)

(1-3) I can see clear-ly now,— the rain— has gone.— I can see all-
(2) I think I can make-it now,— the pain— has gone.— All of the bad-

ob-stac-les in my way,— Gone are the dark
feel-ings have dis-ap-peared,— Here is the rain-

clouds that had me blind
-bow I've been pray-ing for

It's gon-na be a bright,

Copyright © 1972 by CAYMAN MUSIC LTD., c/o COPYRIGHT SERVICE BUREAU LTD.,
221 West 57th Street, New York, N.Y. 10019, U.S.A.
RONDOR MUSIC (LONDON) LIMITED, 147 Oxford Street, London, W.1., England, for the United Kingdom of
Great Britain, Northern Ireland, Eire, the British Commonwealth (excluding Canada and Australasia), Israel,
and all countries throughout Europe

International Copyright Secured
Used by permission

Made in U.S.A.

All Rights Reserved

bright — sun shin-y day, _____ It's gon-na be a bright,

bright — sun shin-y day. _____

Look all a-round — there's noth-ing but blue sky, _____
cresc.

Look straight a-head — noth-ing but blue sky.

It's gon-na be a bright, bright sun shin-y day.

poco dim.

D.S. al Coda

Recorded by HAROLD MELVIN & THE BLUE NOTES on PHILADELPHIA INTERNATIONAL Records

WAKE UP EVERYBODY

Words and Music by
G. McFADDEN
J. WHITEHEAD
V. CARSTARPHEN

Moderately slow

Verse:

1. Wake up ev-'ry-bod-y no more sleep-in' in bed,___
2. Wake up all the doc-tors make the ol' peo-ple well,___

No more back-ward think-in', time for think-in' a-head.___ The
They're the ones who suf-fer an' who catch all the hell.___ But

world has changed_ so ver-y much_ from what it used_ to be,
they don't have_ so ver-y long_ be-fore the Judge-ment Day, So

2650

Copyright © 1975 MIGHTY THREE MUSIC
All rights administered by BLACKWOOD MUSIC INC., 51 West 52nd Street, New York, New York
International Copyright Secured   Made in U.S.A.   All Rights Reserved
Used by permission

There is so much ha-tred, war an' pov-er-ty.
won't-cha make them hap-py be-fore they pass a-way.

Wake up all the teach-ers time to teach a new way,
Wake up all the build-ers time to build a new land,

may-be then they'll lis-ten to what-cha have to say. 'Cause
I know we can do it if we all lend a hand. The

they're the ones who's com-ing up an' the world is in their hands,
on-ly thing we have to do is put it in our mind,

when you teach the chil - dren, teach 'em the ver - y best you can.
sure - ly things will work out, they do it ev - 'ry time.

Chorus:
The world won't get no bet - ter if we just let it be,

The world won't get no bet - ter we got - ta

change it yeah, just you an' me.

D.S. (lyric 1) and fade on Chorus

PIANO MAN

Recorded by BILLY JOEL on COLUMBIA Records

Words and Music by
BILLY JOEL

Moderately

1st time, directly to verse

Last time, Fine

slower

| C | Em (B Bass) | Am | C (G Bass) |

1. It's nine o-clock on a Sat-ur-day, The
(2. Now) John at the bar is a friend of mine, He
(3. Now) Paul is a real-es-tate nov-el-ist, Who
(4. It's a) pret-ty good crowd for a Sat-ur-day, And the

2650

Copyright © 1973, 1974 by HOME GROWN MUSIC, INC. and TINKER STREET TUNES
Rights in the U.S.A. and Canada administered by BLACKWOOD MUSIC, Inc.
International Copyright Secured Made in U.S.A. All Rights Reserved
Used by permission

reg - u - lar crowd shuf - fles in   There's an old man
gets me my drinks for free,   And he's quick with a
nev - er had time for a wife   And he's talk - in' with
man - ag - er gives me a smile   'Cause he knows that it's

sit - ting next to me   Mak - in' love to his ton - ic and
joke or to light up your smoke   But there's some - place that he'd rath - er
Dav - y who's still in the Na - vy And prob - ab - ly will be for
me they've been com - in' to see To for - get a - bout life for a

gin.
be.   He says, "Son, can you
life.   He says, "Bill, I be -
while.   And the wait - ress is
           And the pia - no

2650

play me a mem-o-ry? I'm not real-ly sure how it
lieve this is kill-ing me," As a smile ran a-way from his
prac-tic-ing pol-i-tics, As the bus-'ness-men slow-ly get
sounds like a car-ni-val And the mic-ro-phone smells like a

goes, But it's sad and it's sweet and I knew it com-
face "Well, I'm sure that I could be a mov-ie
stoned Yes, they're shar-ing a drink they call lone-li-
beer And they sit at the bar and put bread in my

plete When I wore a young-er man's clothes."
star If I could get out of this place."
ness But it's bet-ter than drink-in' a-lone.
jar And say "Man, what are you do-in' here?"

Da da da_____ de de da_____ da da_____
Da da da_____ de de da_____ da da_____
*Instrumental*_____
Da da da_____ de de da_____ da da_____

_____ de de da_____ da da_____
_____ de de da_____ da da_____
_____ de de da_____ da da_____

Sing us a song, you're the pia-no man_____

Sing us a song to-night.

Well, we're all in the mood for a mel-o-dy,

And you've got us feel-in' al-right.

2. Now
3. Now
4. It's a

D. C. al Fine

YOU'LL NEVER FIND ANOTHER LOVE LIKE MINE

Recorded by LOU RAWLS on PHILADELPHIA INTERNATIONAL Records

Words and Music by
KENNY GAMBLE
LEON HUFF

Moderately

1. You'll nev-er find, as long as you live, Some-one who loves you ten-der like I do.
2. You'll nev-er find, It'll take the end of all time, Some-one to un-der-stand you like I do.
3. You'll nev-er find an-oth-er love like mine, Some-one who needs you like I do.

2650

Copyright © 1976 MIGHTY THREE MUSIC
All rights administered by BLACKWOOD MUSIC INC., New York, N.Y.
International Copyright Secured   Made in U.S.A.   All Rights Reserved
Used by permission

D D6 D D6 Dmaj7
You'll nev-er find, no mat-ter where you search, Some-one who
You'll nev-er find the rhy - thm, the rhyme; All the
You'll nev-er see what you found in me. You'll keep
D6 Dmaj7
cares a-bout you the way I do. Oh, I'm not
mag - ic we shared, just us two. Oh, I'm not
search - ing and search-ing your whole life through. Oh, I don't
Em9 (A bass)
To Coda
brag - gin' on my - self, ba - by. But I'm the one who loves you, and there's
try - in' to make you stay, ba - by. But I know some-how, some day, some
wish you no bad luck, ba - by. But there's no if's an' but's or

103

1. no one else. No one else.

2. way,

Em9 (A bass)
You are, you're gon-na miss my lov-in',
(You are gon-na miss my lov-in'___)

You're gon-na miss my love.
(You're gon-na miss my lov-in'___) (You're gon-na miss my lov-in')

2650

You're gon-na miss, you're gon-na miss my love.

Oh, (You're gon-na miss my lov-in') Late in the mid-night hour, ba-by,

(You're gon-na miss my lov-in') When it's cold out-side,

(You're gon-na miss my lov-in') You're gon-na miss, you're gon-na miss my love.

D6
Dmaj7
Em9
(A bass)
D. S. al Coda
Repeat and fade
Coda
Em9
(A bass)
(You're gon - na miss my lov - in')
may-be's.
Late in the mid-night hour, ba - by,
(You're gon - na miss my lov - in')
When it's cold out - side,
(You're gon - na miss my lov - in'
You're gon-na
)
miss, you're gon - na miss my love.
Dmaj7
D
Oh,

THERE'S A KIND OF HUSH
(All Over The World)

Recorded by THE CARPENTERS on A&M Records

Words and Music by
LES REED
GEOFF STEPHENS

Medium tempo (With a beat)

There's A Kind Of Hush All O-ver The World— To-night— all o-ver the world— You can hear the sounds— of lov-ers in love— You know what I mean.— Just the two of us and no-bod-y else— in sight—

Copyright © 1966, 1967 DONNA MUSIC LTD., London, England
Rights for the United States and Canada controlled by GLENWOOD MUSIC CORP., Hollywood, California
International Copyright Secured   Made in U.S.A.   All Rights Reserved
Used by permission

There's no-bod-y else___ and I'm feel-ing good___ just hold-ing you tight.___

So lis-ten ver-y care-ful-ly___

Clos-er now___ and you___ will see___ what I mean___ It is-n't a dream.___

The on-ly sound___ that you will hear___ Is

when I whis-per in your ear. I love you, for-ev-er and ev-er. There's A Kind Of Hush All O-ver The World To-night all o-ver the world You can hear the sounds of lov-ers in love.

1.
2. There's A

LOVE REALLY HURTS WITHOUT YOU

Recorded by BILLY OCEAN on ARIOLA AMERICA Records

Words and Music by
BEN FINDON
LES CHARLES

1. You run a-round town like a fool and you think that it's groov-y,
2. (You) walk like a dream, and you make like you're Queen of the ac-tion,

You're giv-in' it to some oth-er guy who gives you the eye you
You're us-ing ev-'ry trick in the book the way that you look you're

Copyright © 1974, 1976 BLACK SHEEP MUSIC INC., Los Angeles, California
International Copyright Secured   Made in U.S.A.   All Rights Reserved
Used by permission

don't give noth-in' to me. You paint-ed a smile and you dress
real-ly some-thing to see. You cheat and you lie to im-press

all the while to ex-cite me but don't you know you're
an-y guy that you fan-cy but don't you know I'm

turn-ing me on I know that it's wrong, but I can't stop this pain in-side me.
out of my mind so give me a sign, and help to ease the pain in-side me. } Ba-

Chorus:
by, love real-ly hurts with-out you love real-ly hurts with-out you

And it's break-ing my heart ___ but what can I do? ___ Ba - by,

love real - ly hurts __ with-out you _____ love real - ly hurts __ through and through __

and it's break-ing my heart, __ But what can I do __ with-out you? __

1.
2. *D. S. and fade ad lib.*
2. You Ba -

THE RUBBERBAND MAN

Recorded by THE SPINNERS on ATLANTIC Records

Words and Music by
LINDA CREED
THOM BELL

Moderately

Hand me down my walk-in' cane, hand me down my hat,

Hur-ry now and don't be late 'cause we ain't got time to chat.

You and me were go-in' out to catch the lat-est sounds,

Copyright © 1976 by MIGHTY THREE MUSIC
All rights administered by BLACKWOOD MUSIC INC., 51 West 52nd Street, New York, New York
International Copyright Secured   Made in U.S.A.   All Rights Reserved
Used by permission

guar-an-teed to blow your mind so high you won't come down.

Hey y'all pre-pare your-self for the rub-ber band man,

You've nev-er heard a sound like the rub-ber band man,

You're bound to lose con-trol when the rub-ber band starts to jam.

Once I went to hear them play at a club outside of town, I was so surprised I was hypnotized by the sound these cats put down. When I saw this short fat guy stretch a band

- be-tween his toes, ___ hey, I laughed so hard 'cause the band got down when it fi-n'ly reached his nose. ___

Do doop doop doop doop do doop do doop.

Do doop doop doop doop do doop do doop.

Do doop doop doop doop do doop do doop do doop. Doop doop doop do doop.

HELP ME RHONDA

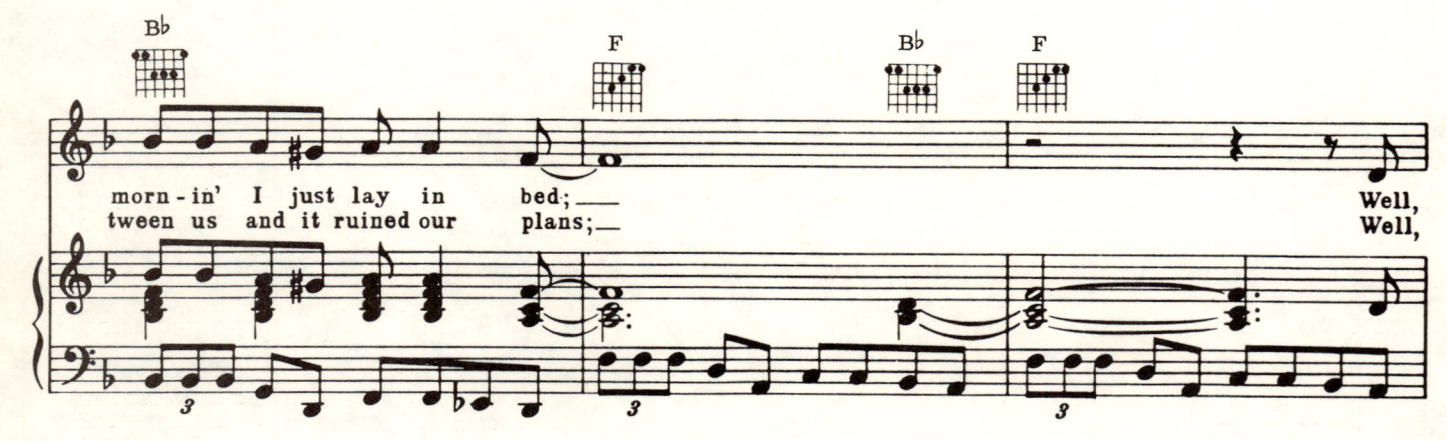

Recorded by THE BEACH BOYS on CAPITOL Records

Words and Music by
BRIAN WILSON

Medium rock

VERSE

1. Since she put me down I've been out do-in' in my head,
2. gon-na be my wife and I was gon-na be her man,

Come in late at night and in the
But she let an-oth-er guy come be-

morn-in' I just lay in bed;
tween us and it ruined our plans;

Well,
Well,

Rhon-da you look so fine, And I know it would-n't take much time, For you to
Rhon-da you caught my eye, And I'll give you lots of rea-sons why, You got-ta

Copyright © 1965 & 1974 by IRVING MUSIC, INC., Hollywood, California
International Copyright Secured   Made in U.S.A.   All Rights Reserved
Used by permission

117

help me, Rhon-da, Help me get her out of my heart.

CHORUS

Help me, Rhon-da! Help, Help me, Rhon-da! Help me, Rhon-da!

Help, Help me, Rhon-da! Help me, Rhon-da! Help, Help me, Rhon-da!

Help me, Rhon-da! Help, Help me, Rhon-da! Help me, Rhon-da!

2650

F
Help, Help me, Rhon - da! Help me, Rhon - da! Help, Help me, Rhon - da!
Gm7
C9
1 F
Help me, Rhon-da! Yeah, get her out of my heart.
mf
2. She was
2 F
C7
Help me, Rhon - da!
f
F
Repeat and fade out
Help, Help me, Rhon - da! Help me, Rhon - da! Help, Help me, Rhon - da!

Recorded by OLIVIA NEWTON-JOHN on MCA Records

IF YOU LOVE ME
(Let Me Know)

Words and Music by
JOHN ROSTILL

Moderate

You came when I was hap-py; in your sun-shine. I grew to love you more each pass-ing day. Be-fore too long I built my world a-round you. And I prayed you'd love e-nough of me to

2650

Copyright © 1974 by Petal Music Ltd., London, England
All rights for the U.S.A. and Canada assigned to AL GALLICO MUSIC CORP., 65 W. 55th St., New York, N.Y. 10019
This arrangement Copyright © 1974 by AL GALLICO MUSIC CORP.
International Copyright Secured   Made in U.S.A.   All Rights Reserved
Used by permission

stay. If you love me let me know. If you don't then let me go. I can't take another minute of a day without you in it. If you love me, let it be, If you don't then set me free.

Take the chains a-way that keep me lov-in' you. The arms that o-pen wide to hold me clos-er; The hands that run their fin-gers through my hair; The smile that says hel-lo, it's good to see you. Any time I turn a-round to find you there. It's this and so much more that makes me love you. What else can I do to make you see? You

F
know you have what - ev - er's mine to give you, but a
Gm
C7
F
D.S. 𝄋 al 𝄌 Coda
F7
love af - fair for one can nev - er be. If you
Coda
B♭
F
Ah! Take the chains
C7
C7
B♭
F
a - way that keep me lov - in' you.
rit.

Recorded by THE JAMES GANG on ABC Records

WALK AWAY

Words and Music by
JOE WALSH

(Chorus)
Em
C
Em
me you don't wan - na talk a - bout it, seems to me you just
me talk all night here comes the morn - ing, seems to me you just
C
D
G
A
turn your pret - ty head and WALK A - WAY.
for - get what we said and greet the day.
Bb
To Coda
A
1 G
C
G
C
2 G
C
G
C
D.S. al Coda
I've got to
Coda
A
Asus
G
WALK A - WAY.

WHY ME?

Recorded by KRIS KRISTOFFERSON on MONUMENT Records

Words and Music by
KRIS KRISTOFFERSON

Moderately, with a Gospel feeling

Why me, Lord? What have I ev-er done to de-serve e-ven one of the pleas-ures I've known? Tell me, Lord, What did I ev-er do that was worth lov-ing you, Or the kind-ness you've shown?

If you think there's a way I can try to re-pay all I've tak-en from you, May-be, Lord, I can show some-one else what I've been thru my-self, On my way back to you.

Copyright © 1972 RESACA MUSIC PUBLISHING CO., 35 Music Square East, Nashville, Tennessee 37203
International Copyright Secured   Made in U.S.A.   All Rights Reserved
Used by permission

C G D7
Lord, help me, Je - sus, I've wast - ed it so, Help me, Je - sus, I know what I
G G7 C G
am. But now that I know that I've need - ed you So, help me
D7 to Coda 1. G D7 2. G G7 D.S. al Coda
Je - sus, my soul's in your hands. Try me, Lord hands.
Coda
G D7 C Bm Am G
hands. Je - sus, my soul's in your hands.
slower

I DO, I DO, I DO, I DO, I DO

Recorded by ABBA on ATLANTIC Records

Words and Music by
BENNY ANDERSSON
STIG ANDERSON
BJORN ULVAEUS

Love me or leave me. Make your choice, but believe me, I love you, I do, I do, I do, I do, I do.

Let's get together. Ev'ry day will be better.

I can't conceal
Leave it or take

C
Csus4
C
A7
Dm
G
it. Don't you see, can't you feel it? Don't you, too? I
it. I be - lieve we can make it.
3
3
3
C
F
C
do, I do, I do, I do, I do.
Oh, I've
Oh, no
Gm
C7
F
F (E Bass)
been dream - in' through my lone - ly past.
hard feel - ings be - tween you and me.
F (D Bass)
F (C Bass)
D7
Dm7
Now I just made it, I found you at
If we can't make it, but just wait and

last.) So come on now let's try ____ it. I love you, can't de-ny __
see.}

it, __ 'cause it's true. __ I do, I do, I do, I do, I

do. _____

YOU MAKE ME FEEL BRAND NEW

Recorded by THE STYLISTICS on AVCO Records

Words and Music by
THOM BELL
LINDA CREED

Slowly

My love,— I'll nev-er find the words, my love, to tell you how I feel, my
My love,— when-ev-er I was in-se-cure, you built me up and made me

love. Mere words— could not— ex-plain.— Pre-cious
sure. You gave— my pride— back to me.— Pre-cious

Copyright © 1974 MIGHTY THREE MUSIC
All rights administered by BLACKWOOD MUSIC INC., 51 West 52nd Street, New York, N.Y. 10019
International Copyright Secured   Made in U.S.A.   All Rights Reserved
Used by permission

love, you held my life with-in your hands, cre - a - ted ev-'ry-thing I__ am
friend, with you I'll al-ways have a friend, you're some-one who I can de - pend to

taught me how to live a - gain. On - ly you__
walk a path that some - times_ bends. With-out you__

(falsetto)

cared when I need - ed a friend,__ be - lieved in me thru_ thick and thin.__
life has no mean-ing or rhyme__ like notes to a song_ out of time.__

This song is for you, filled with grat - i - tude and love:_____
How can I re-pay you for hav-ing faith in me?_____

God bless you, you make me feel brand new, for God blessed me with you;

You make me feel brand new, I sing this song {'cause you / for you}

make me feel___ brand___ new.

D. S. al Coda

Coda *Repeat and fade*

KILLING ME SOFTLY WITH HIS SONG

Recorded by ROBERTA FLACK on ATLANTIC Records

Words by
NORMAN GIMBEL

Music by
CHARLES FOX

Moderately

1. I heard he sang a good song, I heard he had a style.
2. I felt all flushed with fever, em-bar-rassed by the crowd,
3. He sang as if he knew me, in all my dark des-pair.

And so I came to see him to
I felt he found my let-ters and
And then he looked right through me as

Copyright © 1972 by Charles Fox and Norman Gimbel
FOX-GIMBEL PRODUCTIONS, INC., Box 1138, Beverly Hills, California 90213
International Copyright Secured   Made in U.S.A.   All Rights Reserved
Used by permission

lis - ten for a - while. And there he was
read each one out loud. I prayed that he
if I was-n't there. But he was there.

this young boy a stran - ger to my eyes.
would fin - ish but he just kept right on.
this stran - ger sing - ing clear and strong.

Strum - ming my pain with his fin - gers,

Sing - ing my life with his words.

Killing me soft - ly with his song, Killing me soft - ly with his song. Tell - ing my whole life with his words, Kill - ing me soft - ly with his song.

ME AND BOBBY McGEE

Recorded by JANIS JOPLIN on COLUMBIA Records

Words and Music by
KRIS KRISTOFFERSON
FRED FOSTER

Busted flat in Baton Rouge, Headin' for the trains; Feelin' nearly faded as my jeans, Bobby thumbed a diesel down just before it rained; Took us all the way to New Orleans. I took my har-

coal mines of Kentucky To the California sun, Bobby shared the secrets of my soul; Standin' right beside me, Lord, Through everything I done, And every night she kept me from the cold. Then somewhere near Sa-

Copyright © 1969 by COMBINE MUSIC CORPORATION, 35 Music Square East, Nashville, Tennessee 37203
International Copyright Secured   Made in U.S.A.   All Rights Reserved
Used by permission

poon out of my dir-ty, red ban-dan-na And was blow-in' sad while Bob-by sang the
lin-as, Lord, I let her slip a - way Look-in' for the home I hope she'll

blues; With them wind-shield wi-pers slap-pin' time and Bob-by clap-pin'
find; And I'd trade all of my to-mor-rows for a sin-gle yes-ter-

hands We fin-'ly sang up ev-'ry song that driv-er knew.
day, Hold-in' Bob-by's bod-y next to mine.

Free-dom's just an - oth-er word for noth-in' left to lose,
Free-dom's just an - oth-er word for noth-in' left to lose,

G7
C
Noth-in' ain't worth noth-in', but it's free;
Noth-in' left is all she left for me;
F
C
Feel-in' good was eas-y, Lord, When Bob-by sang the blues;
G7
And feel-in' good was good e-nough for me,
And, bud-dy, that was good e-nough for me,
Good e-nough for
1. C
2. C
me and Bob-by Mc-Gee.
From the Gee.
rall.

LIVIN' THING

Recorded by ELECTRIC LIGHT ORCHESTRA on UNITED ARTISTS Records

Words and Music by
JEFF LYNNE

Moderately, with a beat

1. Sail - in' a - way___ on the crest___ of a wave,___ it's like mag - ic.
2. Mak - in' be - lieve___ this is what___ you con - ceived___ from your worst___ day.
3. Tak - in' a dive___ 'cause you can't___ halt the slide___ float - ing down - stream.

Oh, roll - in' and rid - in' and slip - pin' and slid - in', it's mag - ic.
Oh, mov - ing in line,___ then you look___ back in time___ to the first___ day.
Oh, so let her go,___ don't start spoil - ing the show___ it's a bad___ dream.

And

Copyright © 1976 UNITED ARTISTS MUSIC LTD. and JET MUSIC INCORPORATED
All rights for the U.S.A. and Canada administered by UNART MUSIC CORPORATION, New York, New York
International Copyright Secured   Made in U.S.A.   All Rights Reserved
Used by permission

you _____ and your sweet de-sire, _____ You took me, _____ oh, _____ high-er and high-er, ba-by. It's a Liv-in' Thing! It's a ter-ri-ble thing to _____

C
Am
F
lose. It's a giv - en thing, What a ter -
D7
G+
1.2. C
Bbm
ri - ble thing to lose.
F
G
3. C
lose. It's a Liv -
Fade out
Am
F
D7
G7+5
C
in' Thing! It's a ter - ri - ble thing to lose. It's a giv -
en thing. What a ter - ri - ble thing to lose. It's a Liv -

Recorded by DONNY & MARIE OSMOND on MGM Records

Lyric by
MITCHELL PARISH

DEEP PURPLE

Music by
PETER DE ROSE

2650

144

Recorded by CARLY SIMON *and* JAMES TAYLOR *on* ELEKTRA *Records*

MOCKINGBIRD

Additional Lyrics by
JAMES TAYLOR

Words and Music by
INEZ FOXX
CHARLIE FOXX

Moderate beat

Ev-er-y-bod-y have you heard? He's gon-na buy me a mock-ing-bird,

And if that mock-ing-bird won't sing, he's gon-na buy

me a dia-mond ring, And if that dia-mond ring won't shine,

2650

Copyright © 1963, 1974 UNART MUSIC CORPORATION, New York, N.Y.
Made in U.S.A.
International Copyright Secured   All Rights Reserved
Used by permission

F
C7
he's gon-na sure - ly break this heart of mine,
And that's why I keep on
B♭7
C7
Tacet
F
tell - in' ev - 'ry - bod - y, say - in' wo, wo, wo, wo, wo.
Hear me now and un - der-stand
C7
he's gon-na find me some peace of mind.
And if that peace of mind won't stay,
F
F7
I'm gon-na find my-self a bet - ter way.
And if that

Well, now, everybody have you heard?
She's gonna buy me a mocking bird
If that mocking bird don't sing,
She's gonna buy me a diamond ring.
And if that diamond ring won't shine
Guess it surely break this poor heart of mine,
And that's the reason why I keep on tellin' everybody sayin'
No, no, no, no, no, no, no, no.

Listen now and understand
She's gonna find me some peace of mind.
And if that peace of mind won't stay,
I'm gonna get myself a better way
I might rise above, I might go below,
Ride with the tide and go with the flow,
And that's the reason why I keep on shouting in your ears, y'all
No, no, no, no, no, no, now, now, baby.

Recorded by THE MANHATTANS on COLUMBIA Records

KISS AND SAY GOODBYE

Words and Music by
WINFRED LOVETT

Recitation (Spoken over intro)

This has got to be the saddest day of my life
I called you here today for a bit of bad news
I won't be able to see you any more
Because of my obligations
And the ties that you have
We've been meeting here every day

And since this is our last date together
I want to hold you just one more time
When you turn and walk away don't look back
I want to remember you just like this
Let's just kiss and say goodbye.

Moderately slow

I had to meet you here to-day, _____ there's just so man-y things to say,

Please don't stop me till I'm through, _____ this is some-thing I hate to do. _____

Copyright © 1976 BLACKWOOD MUSIC INC. and NATTAHNAM MUSIC CO.
All rights Administered by BLACKWOOD MUSIC INC., 51 West 52nd Street, New York, New York
International Copyright Secured   Made in U.S.A.   All Rights Reserved
Used by permission

We've been meet-ing here so long, I guess what we done was wrong. Please, dar-ling, don't you cry, Let's just kiss and say good-bye. Man-y months have passed us by, I'm gon-na miss you I can't lie. I've got ties and so do you,_____ I just think this is the thing__ to do.

It's gon-na hurt me I can't lie,_____ may-be you'll meet___ an-oth-er guy.____ Un-der-stand me won't you try, try, try,___ Let's just kiss and say____ good-bye.____

poco rit.

IN THE WINTER

Recorded by JANIS IAN on COLUMBIA Records

Words and Music by
JANIS IAN

Slowly

The days are o-kay. I watch the T.V. in the af-ter-noon. If I get lone-ly, the sound of oth-er voic-es, oth-er rooms are near to me. I'm not a-fraid.

---

* Chord symbols in Roman type are for piano. Chord symbols in italics are for guitar. Janis plays in A minor with a capo across the 3rd fret.

2650

Copyright © 1974,1975 MINE MUSIC LTD. and APRIL MUSIC INC., New York, N.Y.
International Copyright Secured   Made in U.S.A.   All Rights Reserved
Used by permission

Amsus2
CmaddD
The op-er-a - tor, she tells the time it's good for a laugh.
Dmsus2
FmaddG
Amsus2
CmaddD
3
There's al-ways ra - di - o.
Dm
Fm
Am
Cm
And for a dime I can talk to God, dial a prayer,
E7sus4
G7sus4
E7
G7
Am
Cm
Fmaj7
Abmaj7
E7sus4
G7sus4
E7
G7
are you there, do you care? Are you there?

And in the win-ter ex-tra blan-kets for the cold. Fix the heat-er, get-ting old. I am wis-er now you know and still as big a fool con-cern-ing you. I met your friend She's ver-y nice, what can I say?

It was an accident; I never dreamed we'd meet again this way. You're looking well. I'm not afraid. You have a lovely home. Just like a picture. No, I live alone. I found it easier. You must remember how I never liked the party life.

Up all night. Love-ly wife. You have a love-ly wife. ____ And in the win-ter ex-tra blan-kets for the cold. ___ Fix the heat-er, get-ting old. ___ You are with her now ___ I know ___ I'll live a-lone for-ev-er, not to-geth-er now.

Recorded by MICHEL LEGRAND
From the United Artists Motion Picture "PIECES OF DREAMS"

LITTLE BOY LOST
(Pieces Of Dreams)

Lyric by
MARILYN and ALAN BERGMAN

Music by
MICHEL LEGRAND

Lit-tle Boy Lost _____ in search of Lit-tle Boy Found. _____ You go a-won-der-ing, wan-der-ing, stum-bl-ing, tum-bl-ing, round! round!

When will you find _____ what's on the tip of your mind? _____

Copyright © 1970 UNITED ARTISTS MUSIC CO., INC., 729 Seventh Avenue, New York, N.Y. 10019
International Copyright Secured   Made in U.S.A.   All Rights Reserved
Used by permission

Why are you blind to all you ev-er were, nev-er were, real-ly are, near-ly are? Lit-tle Boy False in search of Lit-tle Boy True. Will you be ev-er done trav-el-ling, al-ways un-rav-el-ling you, you? Run-ning a-way could lead you fur-ther a-stray And as for

fish-ing in streams ___ for piec-es of dreams, ___ Those
piec-es will nev-er fit. What is the sense of it? Lit-tle Boy Blue, ___ don't let your
lit-tle sheep roam. ___ It's time, come blow your horn, meet the morn,
Look and see, can you be far from home? ___

158

Recorded by WILLIE NELSON on COLUMBIA Records

REMEMBER ME
(When The Candle Lights Are Gleaming)

Words and Music by
SCOTT WISEMAN

Moderato

Verse

The sweet-est songs be-long to lov-ers in the gloam-ing,
once that you were mine a-lone for-ev-er

The sweet-est days were the days that used to be,
And I was yours 'till the end of e-ter-ni-ty,

The sad-dest words I ev-er heard were words of part-ing
But all our vows are bro-ken now and you will nev-er

2650

International Copyright Secured
Used by permission

Copyright © 1946 (Renewed) by VOGUE MUSIC INC.
Made in U.S.A.

All Rights Reserved

F6 Ab7 C Cm G7 C
When you said "Sweet - heart, RE - MEM - BER ME"
Be the same ex - cept in mem - o - ry.
Chorus
C G7 C7 F C
RE-MEM-BER ME when the can - dle lights are gleam - ing, RE-MEM-BER
when I'm gone, for I'll be yearn - ing, For you each
mf
G7 Dm7 G7 G7+5 C C G7 C7 F
ME at the close of a long long day. It would be so sweet when
night far a - way on the deep blue sea. Don't cry for me but
C Em Dm7 C C7 F6 Ab7 C Cm
all a - lone I'm dream - ing Just to know you
keep our love light burn - ing. When I'm gone, sweet -
G7 1. C F C Cdim G7 2 C F C
still RE-MEM-BER ME.
heart, RE-MEM-BER You told me ME.
f

Recorded by FREDDY FENDER on ABC/DOT Records

WASTED DAYS AND WASTED NIGHTS

Words and Music by
WAYNE M. DUNCAN
FREDDY FENDER

2650

left me. I was so lonely prayed for you only, my love. Why should I keep loving you when I know that you're not true, And why should I call your name when you're the blame for making me blue.

YOU'RE MY BEST FRIEND

Recorded by QUEEN on ELEKTRA Records

Words and Music by
JOHN DEACON

With a beat

1. Ooh, you make me live___ What-ev-er this world can give to me.___ It's you, you're all I___ see.___ Ooh, you make me live___ now, hon-ey, Ooh, you make me live.___
2. Ooh, you make me live___ When-ev-er this world is cruel to me.___ I got you to help me for-give.___ Ooh, you make me live___ now, hon-ey, Ooh, you make me live.___

Copyright © 1975 by B. FELDMAN AND CO., LTD., trading as TRIDENT MUSIC
138-140 Charing Cross Road, London WC2H 0ld, England
Distributed exclusively in the U.S.A. and Canada by THE BIG 3 MUSIC CORPORATION
International Copyright Secured   Made in U.S.A.   All Rights Reserved
Used by permission

Ooh, you're the best friend that I ev-er had.
I've been with you such a long time, You're my sun-shine and I want you to know that my feel-ings are true, I real-ly love you.

Ooh, you're the first one when things turn out bad.
You know I'll nev-er be lone-ly, You're my on-ly one and I love the things, I real-ly love the things that you do.

Oh, You're My Best Friend.

Dm7 (C bass)
C
E (G♯bass)
Ooh, you make me live. Ooh, I've been
Am
C7 (B♭bass)
F
Fm6
wan - der - ing round, But I still come back to you, In
G
E (G♯bass)
Am
D
G
rain or shine you've stood by me, girl, I'm hap - py at home,
C
You're My Best Friend.
1.
2.

Fm6
C
Fm6
Ooh,
Ooh, You're My Best
C
Dm7 (C bass)
C
Friend.
Ooh, you make me live,
3
Dm7 (C bass)
C
G
C
G
C
Ooh, You're My Best Friend.
G
C
G
C
3

RIGHT BACK WHERE WE STARTED FROM

Recorded by MAXINE NIGHTINGALE on UNITED ARTISTS Records

Words and Music by
PIERRE TUBBS
VINCENT EDWARDS

Moderately, with a strong beat

Oo,— and it's all_____ right, and it's com-in' 'long;— we got-ta get right back to where we_____ start-ed from._____

Copyright © 1975, 1976 ATV MUSIC, LTD. and UNIVERSAL SONGS
All rights controlled in the U.S.A. and Canada by ATV MUSIC CORP., 6255 Sunset Blvd., Hollywood, Ca. 90028 and
UNART MUSIC CORPORATION, 6920 Sunset Blvd., Hollywood, Ca. 90028
International Copyright Secured   Made in U.S.A.   All Rights Reserved
Used by permission

Love is good, love can be strong; we gotta get right back to where we started from, uh huh.

Do you remember that day
A love like ours

when you first came my way? I said no one
can nev-er fade a-way. You know it's on-
could take your place.
ly just be-gun.

And if you get hurt by the lit-tle things
You give me your love, I just can't stay
I say, I can put that smile back on your
a-way; I know you are the on-ly

B♭
1.
2.
face. Oo, and it's Oo, and it's
one.
Repeat and fade
C
B♭
all right, and it's com-in' 'long; we got-ta get right back to where we
Repeat and fade
C
started from. Love is good, love can be strong; we got-ta
B♭
get right back to where we start-ed from. It's

BORN TO RUN

Recorded by BRUCE SPRINGSTEEN *on* COLUMBIA *Records*

Words and Music by
BRUCE SPRINGSTEEN

With a driving beat (♩ = 144)

1. In the day we sweat it out on the streets of a run-a-way A-mer-i-can dream. At night we ride through man-sions of glo-ry in su-i-cide ma-chines. Sprung from cag-es on High-way 9, Chrome wheeled, fuel in-ject-ed, and step-pin' out o-ver the line. Oh, ba-by, this town rips the

Copyright © 1975 LAUREL CANYON MUSIC LTD.
International Copyright Secured   Made in U.S.A.   All Rights Reserved
Used by permission

bones from your back, It's a death trap, it's a su-i-cide rap. We got-ta get out while we're young,

'Cause tramps like us, ba-by, we were Born To Run.

2. Babe, I

2. Wen-dy, want to know if love is real.

2. Wendy, let me in, I wanna be your friend,
   I wanna guard your dreams and visions.
   Just wrap your legs 'round these velvet rims,
   And strap your hands 'cross my engines.
   Together we could break this trap,
   We'll run till we drop, and baby, we'll never go back.
   Oh, will you walk with me out on the wire?
   Cause, baby, I'm just a scared and lonely rider,
   But I gotta know how it feels,
   I want to know if love is wild,
   Babe, I want to know if love is real.

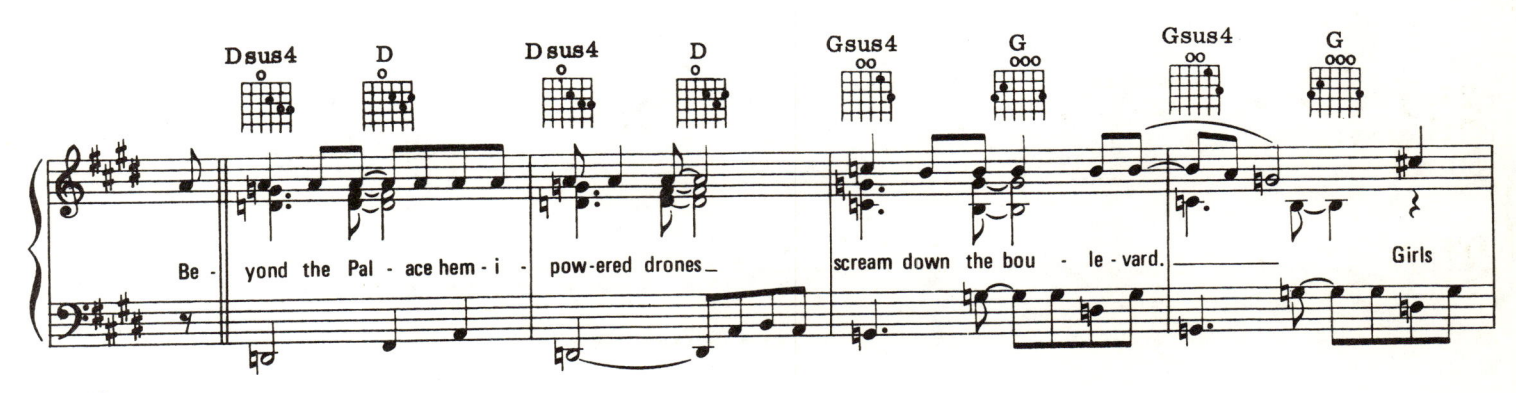

Be-yond the Pal-ace hem-i-pow-ered drones scream down the bou-le-vard. Girls

Asus4 A Asus4 A Csus4 C Csus4 C
comb their hair in rear view mir-rors and the boys try to look so hard. (Sung:) The a-
(Spoken:)
Dsus4 D Dsus4 D Gsus4 G Gsus4 G
muse-ment park ris-es bold and stark as kids are hud-dled on the beach in a mist. I wan-na
Asus4 A Asus4 A Csus4 C Csus4 C
die with you, Wen-dy, on the streets to-night in an ev-er-last-ing kiss.
N. C
E
The high-ways jammed with bro-ken he-roes on a
A B7sus4 B E
last chance pow-er drive. Ev-'ry-bod-y's out on the run to-night, but there's
f

A
B7sus4
B
A
E (G♯bass)
no place left to hide. To - geth - er, Wen - dy, we can live with the sad - ness, I'll
F♯m
E (G♯bass)
E
E9
A
love you with all the mad - ness in my soul. Oh, some day, girl, I
E (G♯bass)
F♯m
E (G♯bass)
E
don't know when, we're gon - na get to that place where we real - ly wan - na go, and we'll walk in the
C♯m
A
B
E
C♯m
sun. But till then, tramps like us, ba - by, we were Born To Run! Ah, hon - ey,
A
B
E
C♯m
tramps like us, ba - by, we were Born To Run! Come on, Wen - dy.
A
B
B11
B7
E
Tramps like us, ba - by, we were Born To Run.

Recorded by ELECTRIC LIGHT ORCHESTRA on UNITED ARTISTS Records

STRANGE MAGIC

Words and Music by
JEFF LYNNE

G
G+
(C bass)
In a bro - ken stone - age dawn,
Mak - ing waves a - cross my time,
Now I've seen the way it's got to end,
G
G+
Em
(G bass)
You fly so high. I get a
Oh no, oh no. I get a
Sweet dream, sweet dream.
Dm7
Em7
Dm7
Chorus:
Strange Mag - ic, Oh, what a Strange Mag -
mf

-ic, Oh, it's a Strange Magic, Got a Strange Magic, Got a Strange Mag-ic. (3. Oh,) ic. It's mag-ic. It's mag-ic. It's mag-ic.

Dm7
Em7
Dm7
Strange Mag - ic, Oh, what a Strange Mag -
mf
Em7
Dm7
Em7
- ic, Oh, it's a Strange Mag - ic, Got a
Am7
D7
G
Am7
D7
Strange Mag - ic, Got a Strange Mag -
Repeat and fade
G
Am7
D7
ic. You know I got a Strange Mag -

Recorded by LOGGINS & MESSINA on COLUMBIA Records

YOUR MAMA DON'T DANCE

By
JIM MESSINA
KENNY LOGGINS

Medium early rock shuffle beat

old folks say that you gotta end your day by ten. If you're out on a date, and you bring it home late, it's a sin. There just ain't no ex-cus-in', you know you're gon-na lose and nev-er win. And, say it a-gain, And it's all be-cause your ma-ma don't dance and your dad-dy don't rock and roll. Your

F7
C
ma - ma don't dance and your dad - dy don't rock and roll.__ When
G7
To Coda
C
eve - nin' rolls a - round and it's time to go to town, where do you go to rock and roll? You
F7
pull in - to a drive - in and find a place to park. You hop in - to the back seat where you
know it's nice and dark.__ You're just a - bout to groove and you're think - in' it's a breeze,__ There's a

light in your eye, and then a guy___ says, "Out-ta the car, long hair, But ooh - wee___ you're com-in' with me, the lo-cal po - lice."

D. S. al Coda

And it's all be-cause your

Coda

go to rock and roll? Where do you go to rock and roll? Where do you go to rock and roll?

HURT

Recorded by ELVIS PRESLEY on RCA Records

Words and Music by
JIMMIE CRANE
AL JACOBS

Moderately *(with expression)*

HURT ___ to think that you lied to me, ___ HURT ___ way down deep in-side of me. ___ You said your love was true and we'd nev-er part, ___ Now you want some-one new and it breaks my heart. ___

Copyright © 1953, 1954 MILLER MUSIC CORPORATION, New York, New York
International Copyright Secured   Made in U.S.A.   All Rights Reserved

I'm HURT_____ much more than you'll ev-er know,_____ HURT_____ be-cause I still love you so._____ But e-ven tho' you've HURT me like no one else could do, I would nev-er, nev-er HURT you._____ you._____

Recorded by JOE COCKER on A&M Records

THE LETTER

Words and Music by
WAYNE CARSON THOMPSON

wrote me a let-ter said she could-n't live__ with-out__ me no more.__

Lis-ten mis-ter can't you see I got to get back__ to my ba-by once more,__ An-y way.

Give me a tick-et for an air-plane, Ain't got time__ to take the fast-est train.

Lone-ly days are gone,__ I'm a-go-in' home,__ My ba-by just wrote__ me a

1. let-ter._____ 2. Well she let-ter.__ *Repeat for fade* My ba-by just wrote__ me a let-ter.__ My

BY THE TIME I GET TO PHOENIX

Recorded by GLEN CAMPBELL on CAPITOL Records

Words and Music by
JIM WEBB

Moderately

1. By the time I get to Phoenix she'll be ris-in'.
(By the) (2.) time I make Al-bu-quer-que she'll be work-in'.
(By the) (3.) time I make Ok-la-ho-ma she'll be sleep-in'.

She'll find the note I left hang-in' on her door.
She'll prob'ly stop at lunch and give me a call.
She'll turn soft-ly and call my name out low.

She'll laugh when she reads the part that says I'm leav-in',
But, she'll just hear that phone keep on ring-in'
And she'll cry just to think I'd real-ly leave her,

Copyright © 1967 by JOHNNY RIVERS MUSIC, Hollywood, California
Copyright assigned 1971 to DRAMATIS MUSIC CORP., New York, N.Y.
International Copyright Secured   Made in U.S.A.   All Rights Reserved
Used by permission

Cm
To Coda
1.
Fm7
Db
'cause I've left that girl so man - y times be - fore.
off the
'tho'
Bb7
2.
Fm7
Db
Bb7
D. S. al Coda
(2.) By the
wall,
that's all.
(3.) By the
CODA
Fm7
Bb7
Ebmaj7
Abmaj7
Fm
time and time I've tried to tell her so,
she just did - n't know,
G
C
Bb
C
Bb
C
I would real - ly go.

KNOCK THREE TIMES

Recorded by TONY ORLANDO & DAWN on BELL Records

Words and Music by
IRWIN LEVINE
L. RUSSELL BROWN

Moderately

Verse:

Hey, girl, what-cha do-in' down there? Danc-in' a-lone ev-'ry night while I live right a-bove you. I can hear your mu-sic play-in', I can feel your bod-y sway-in', One floor be-low me, you don't e-ven know me, I love you.

you look out your win-dow to-night, Pull in the string with the note that's at-tached to my heart. Read how man-y times I saw you, How in my si-lence I a-dore you, And on-ly in my dreams did that wall be-tween us come a-part.

Copyright © 1970 POCKET FULL OF TUNES, INC., 900 Sunset Blvd., Suite 620, Los Angeles, California 90069
International Copyright Secured   Made in U.S.A.   All Rights Reserved
Used by permission

Chorus:
G
D
Oh, my dar - lin', Knock Three Times on the ceil - ing if you want_ me;_
f
A7
Twice on the pipe if the an - swer is
3
D
D7
G
no. Oh, my sweet - ness, (Knock) means you'll meet me in the
D
A7
hall - way;_ Twice on the pipe
Dmaj7
D
1.
2.
G
A7
D.S. and fade
means you ain't gon - na show. 2. If Oh, my dar - lin',
D.S. and fade

SMOKE ON THE WATER

Recorded by DEEP PURPLE on WARNER BROS. Records

Words and Music by
IAN PAICE
JON LORD
IAN GILLAN
RITCHIE BLACKMORE
ROGER GLOVER

Moderately
Chords tacet

con 8 ad lib throughout

1. We all came out to Montreux_ on the Lake Geneva shoreline_ To make records with a mobile we didn't have much time._ Frank Zappa and the Mothers were at the best place around,

But some stu-pid with a flare gun burned the place to the ground.

Smoke on the wa-ter, fire in the sky, Smoke on the wa-ter.

D.C. for additional words

2. They burned down the gambling house
   It died with an awful sound
   Funky and Claude was running in and out
   Pulling kids out the ground
   When it all was over
   We had to find another place
   But Swiss time was running out
   It seemed that we would lose the race
   Smoke on the water, fire in the sky
   Smoke on the water.

3. We ended up at the Grand Hotel
   It was empty cold and bare
   But with the Rolling truck Stones thing just outside
   Making our music there
   With a few red lights and a few old beds
   We made a place to sweat
   No matter what we get out of this
   I know we'll never forget
   Smoke on the water, fire in the sky
   Smoke on the water.

Repeat and fade after 3rd verse

Chords tacet

CANDIDA

Recorded by TONY ORLANDO & DAWN on BELL Records

Words and Music by
TONI WINE
IRWIN LEVINE

Moderately, with a beat

Verse

1. The stars won't come out ___ if they know ___ that you're a-bout, ___ 'cause they could-n't match ___ the glow ___ of your eyes. ___ And oh, who am I, ___ just an or-di-nar-y guy; ___ Try-in' hard ___ to win ___ me first prize. ___ Oh, ___

2. (The) fu-ture is bright, ___ the gyp-sy told ___ me so ___ last night, ___ said she saw our chil-dren play-ing ___ in the sun-shine, ___ And there was you and I, ___ in a house, ba-by, no lie; ___ And all these things ___ were yours ___ and they were mine. ___ Oh, my

Copyright © 1969, 1970 POCKET FULL OF TUNES, INC., 9200 Sunset Blvd., Los Angeles, California 90069
International Copyright Secured Made in U.S.A. All Rights Reserved
Used by permission

Chorus
G
D
Can - di - da, we could make it to - geth - er, the
f
A7
fur - ther from here, girl, the bet - ter, where the air is fresh and
D
D7
G
clean. Can - di - da, just take my hand and I'll
D
A7
lead ya, I prom - ise life will be sweet - er, and it says so in my
1. D
Em (A Bass)
A7
2. D
D7
D.S. and fade
dream. 2. The dream. Oh, Can -
mf
D.S. and fade

VINCENT
(Starry, Starry Night)

Recorded by DON McLEAN on UNITED ARTISTS Records

Words and Music by
DON McLEAN

Moderately

1. Star-ry, star-ry night, paint your pal-ette blue and grey, Look out on a sum-mer's day, with eyes that know the dark-ness in my soul. Shad-ows on the

night, flam-ing flow'rs that bright-ly blaze, Swirl-ing clouds in vio-let haze re-flect in Vin-cent's eyes of Chi-na blue. Col-ors chang-ing

night, por-traits hung in emp-ty halls, Frame-less heads on name-less walls, with eyes that watch the world and can't for-get. Like the stran-gers that you've

Copyright © 1971, 1972 MAYDAY MUSIC, INC. and YAHWEH TUNES, INC.
International Copyright Secured Made in U.S.A. All Rights Reserved
Used by permission

hills,
hue,
met, sketch the trees and the daf-fo-dils,
morn-ing fields of am-ber grain,
the rag-ged men in rag-ged clothes,

Am

Catch the breeze and the win-ter chills, In col-ors on the snow-y lin-en
Weath-ered fac-es lined in pain, Are soothed be-neath the art-ist's lov-ing
The sil-ver thorn of blood-y rose, Lie crushed and bro-ken on the vir-gin

C   **D7**

land.
hand.
snow. Now I un-der-stand
Now I un-der-stand
Now I think I know

G   **C**   **G**   **Am**

what you tried to say to me, How you suf-fered for your
what you tried to say to me, How you suf-fered for your
what you tried to say to me, How you suf-fered for your

D7   **G**   **Em**

san-i-ty, How you tried to set them free. They would not lis-ten, they did
san-i-ty, How you tried to set them free. They would not lis-ten, they did
san-i-ty, How you tried to set them free. They would not lis-ten, they're not

not know how,___ Per-haps they'll lis-ten now.

2. Star-ry, star-ry now. For they could not love you,

But still your love was true, And when no

Am7 Cm6 G F7
hope was left in sight _ on that star - ry, star - ry night, You took your life, as lov - ers of - ten
E7 Am7 C
do; But I could have told you, Vin-cent, This world was nev - er meant for one as
D7 G
D.S. al Coda
beau - ti - ful as you. 3. Star - ry, star - ry
Coda
A7 Am7 D7 G
lis - t'ning still, _ Per - haps they nev - er will. _
rall.

I'D REALLY LOVE TO SEE YOU TONIGHT

Recorded by ENGLAND DAN & JOHN FORD COLEY on BIG TREE Records

Words and Music by
PARKER McGEE

Hel-lo, yeah, it's been a-while. Not much, how 'bout you? I'm not sure why

Dm7
B♭/C
C
— I called, — I guess I real-ly just want-ed to talk to you.
Gm7
3 fr.
C7
Fmaj7
And I was think - in' may - be lat - er on
We could go walk - in' through a wind - y park,
Gm7
3 fr.
C7
Fmaj7
Am7
we could get to-geth - er for a while. It's been — such a long —
take a drive a - long the beach or stay at home and watch —
Dm7
B♭/C
C
time — and I real - ly do miss — your — smile. —
T V, — you see it real - ly does - n't mat - ter much to

me. I'm not talk-in' 'bout mov-in' in and I don't wan-na change your life, but there's a warm wind blow-in' the stars a-round and I'd real-ly love to see you to-night.

2.

I won't ask for prom-is-es,
so you don't have to lie.
We've both played that game be-fore;
say I love you, then say good-bye.

D.S. 𝄋 and fade

DAYDREAM

Recorded by THE LOVIN' SPOONFUL on KAMA SUTRA Records

Words and Music by JOHN B. SEBASTIAN

Moderately

1. What a day for a Day-dream,
2. I've been hav-ing a sweet-dream,
3. (Whistle)

What a day for a day-dream-in' boy.
I've been dream-in' since I woke up to-day.
(Whistle)

And I'm lost in a Day-dream, Dream-in' 'bout my bun-dle of joy.
It's star-ring me and my sweet dream, 'Cause she's the one makes me feel this way.
(Whistle)

And e-ven if time ain't real-ly on my side, It's one of those days for tak-ing a
And e-ven if time is pass-ing me by a lot, I could-n't care less a-bout
And you can be sure that if you're feel-in' right, A Day-dream will last till long

walk out-side. I'm blow-ing the day to take a walk in the sun,
dues you say I got. To-mor-row I'll pay the dues for drop-ping my load,
in-to the night. To-mor-row at break-fast you may pick up your ears,

to Coda ⊕

Copyright © 1966 THE HUDSON BAY MUSIC COMPANY, 1619 Broadway, New York, N.Y. 10019
International Copyright Secured   Made in U.S.A.   All Rights Reserved
Used by permission

Dm7
G7sus4
G7
G7sus4
G7
D.S. al Coda
And fall on my face on some-bod-y's new mowed lawn.
A pie in the face for be-ing a sleep-y bull toad.
Coda
Dm7
G9
C6
C
Or you may be day-dream-in' for a thou-sand years. What a day for a Day-
A7
Dm7
G7
dream, Cus-tom made for a day-dream-in' boy.
C
A7
Dm7
G11
G7
And I'm lost in a Day-dream, Dream-in' 'bout my bun-dle of joy.
F
D7
C
A7
F
D7
C
A7
(Whistle)
(Whistle)
Fade till finish

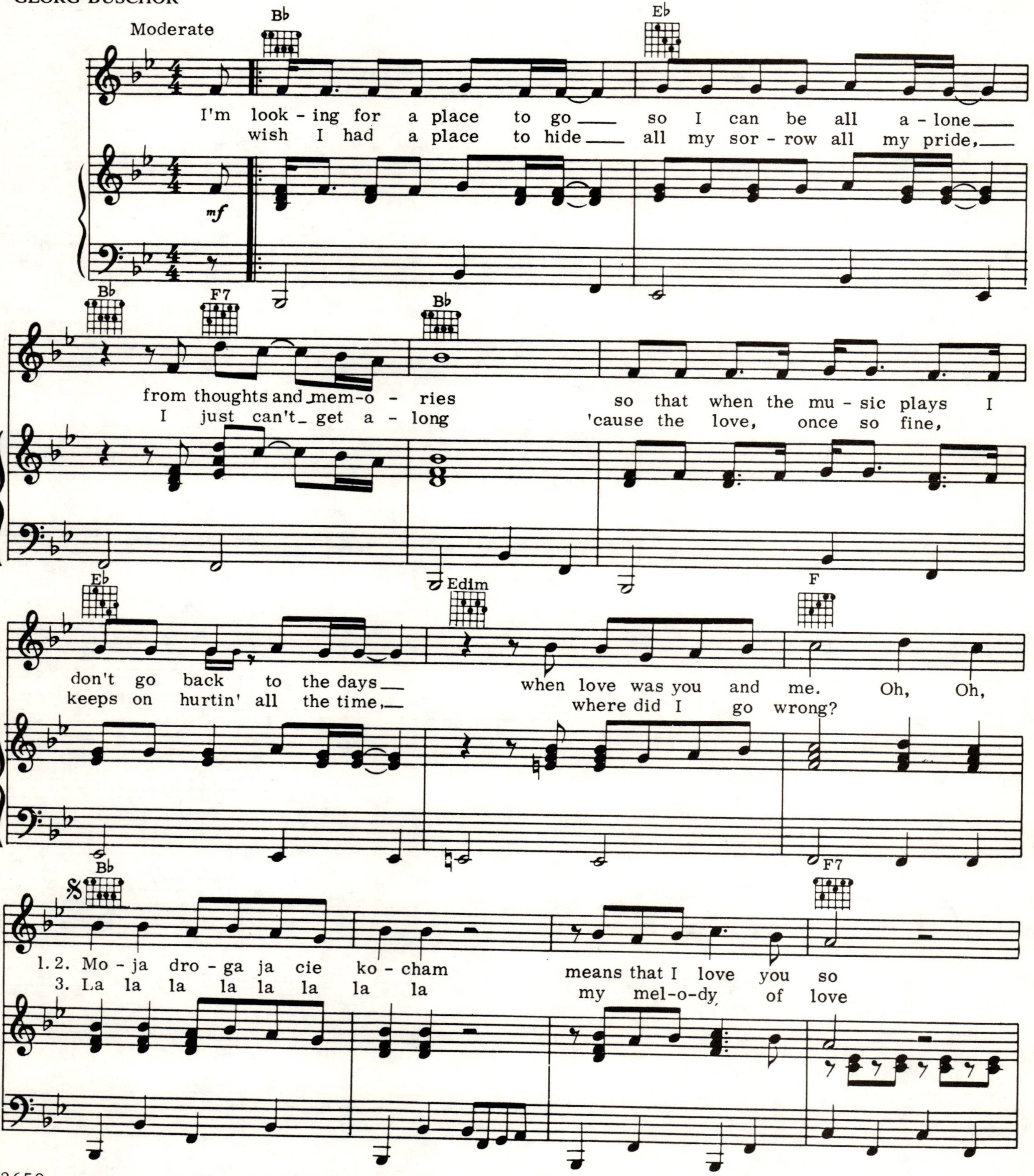

Mo - ja dro-ga ja-cie ko-cham more than you'll ev - er
La la la la la la la la my mel - o - dy of
B♭
know, Ko - cham cie - bie ca - lem ser - ce
love, La la la la la la la la
G7
Cm
E♭
B♭
love you with all my heart re-turn to me and al - ways be
my mel - o - dy of love re-turn to me and al - ways be
F7
1. B♭
F+
2. 3. B♭
F7 D. S. al fade
my mel-o - dy of love. love. Oh, Oh,
my mel-o - dy of love. (fade)

SWEET THING

Recorded by RUFUS featuring CHAKA KHAN on ABC Records

Words and Music by
**TONY MAIDEN
CHAKA KHAN**

1) I will love you any-way ev-en if you can-not stay.
   I think you are the one for me; here is where you ought to be.

   wish you were my lov-er, but you act so "un-der cov-er;"
   to love you, child, my whole life long, be it right or be it wrong.

Copyright © 1975 by AMERICAN BROADCASTING MUSIC, INC., Los Angeles, California
This arrangement Copyright © 1976 by AMERICAN BROADCASTING MUSIC, INC.
International Copyright Secured Made in U.S.A. All Rights Reserved
Used by permission

I just want to sat-is-fy you, though you're not mine, I can't de-ny it.
I'm on-ly what you make me, ba-by, don't walk a-way, don't be sha-dy.

Don't you hear my talk-in', ba-by love me now or I'll go cra-zy.
Don't want your mind, don't want your mon-ey; these words I say, they may sound fun-ny, but

Oh, sweet thing, oh, you know you're my ev-'ry-thing.

Oh, — ah — sweet thing. _____ Oh, — you know, you're my ev - 'ry-thing.

1. Yes, you are. _____ 2.) I

2. Yes, you are. _____

Ah, _____ 3.) You

are my heat, you are my fire, you make me weak with strong desire;

to love you, child, my whole life long, be it right or be it wrong.

I just want to satisfy you though you're not mine, I can't deny it.

Don't you hear me talkin', baby? Love me now or I'll go crazy.

Repeat and fade

HOUND DOG

Recorded by ELVIS PRESLEY on RCA Records

Words and Music by
JERRY LEIBER
MIKE STOLLER

Medium Bright Rock

CHORUS (tacet)

You ain't noth-in' but a Hound Dog, _____ cry-in' all the time.

You ain't noth-in' but a Hound Dog, _____ cry-in' all the time.

Well, — you ain't nev-er caught a rab-bit and you ain't no friend of mine.

Copyright © 1956 by ELVIS PRESLEY MUSIC and LION PUBLISHING COMPANY, INC.
All rights for the United States of America administered by ELVIS PRESLEY MUSIC, New York, N.Y.
International Copyright Secured   Made in U.S.A.   All Rights Reserved
Used by permission

When they said you was high-classed, well, that was just a lie.

When they said you was high-classed, well, that was just a lie.

Well, you ain't never caught a rabbit and you ain't no friend of

1. mine.

2. You ain't nothin' but a mine.

WHOSE GARDEN WAS THIS?

Recorded by JOHN DENVER on RCA Records

Words and Music by TOM PAXTON

Whose Gar-den Was This? __ It must have been love-ly. __

Did it have flow-ers? __ I've seen pic-tures of flow-ers, __

And I'd love to have smelled one! __

Whose riv-er was this? __ You say it ran free-ly? __
Whose gray sky was this? __ Or was it a blue one? __

E
C#m
Blue was its col - or? I've seen blue in some pic - tures, And I'd
Nights there were breez - es? I've heard rec - ords of breez - es, And you
D
F#m
A
love to have been there!
tell me you felt one.
Ah, tell me a - gain, I need to know: The
mf
D
Bm
E7
F#m
for - est had trees, The mead - ows were green, The o - ceans were
E
A
F#m
blue, And birds real - ly flew, Can you swear that was true?
A
C#m
Bm
1.
F#m
2.
F#m
D.S. al Fine
D.S. al Fine

OPERATOR

Recorded by THE MANHATTAN TRANSFER on Atlantic Records

Words and Music by
WILLIAM SPIVERY

Freely

Op-er-a-tor, give me in-for-ma-tion; in-for-ma-tion, give me long ___ dis-tance; long dis-tance, give me heav en. *(two three)* Oh, op-er-a-tor, in-for-ma-tion, give me Je-sus on the

Moderately, with a strong Gospel beat ($\sqrt{}\!\!\!\!\!\sqrt{} = \sqrt{}^3\!\!\!\sqrt{}$)

Copyright © 1959 & 1975 by CONRAD MUSIC, a division of ARC MUSIC CORP., New York, N.Y.
International Copyright Secured   Made in U.S.A.   All Rights Reserved
Used by permission

line, on the line. Op-er-a-tor, in-for-ma-tion, I'd like to speak to a friend of mine. Oh, prayer is the num-ber, faith is the ex-change, heav-en is the street and Je-sus is his name. Oh, op-er-a-tor, in-for-ma-tion, please give me Je-sus on the

D
D
line, on the line. Op - er - a - tor, in - for - ma - tion, tell me
a - tor, in - for - ma - tion, please
G
D
why why, yeah. Op - er - a - tor, in - for -
hur - ry if you can. Op - er - a - tor, in - for -
A7
E7
A
ma - tion, don't try to tell me what num - ber to call. Oh, my
ma - tion, please con - nect me with the man. Oh, don't
D
G
moth - er used this num - ber when I was ver - y small, and ev - 'ry time she dialed it, she
wor - ry 'bout the mon - ey, I will pay the charge; just get me up - on this line, I'm

Gm
D
G
al - ways got a call. Oh, op - er - a - tor, in - for - ma - tion, please
call - in' from my heart. Op - er - a - tor, in - for - ma - tion, please
D
(F♯ Bass)
Em7
G
(A Bass)
1.
D
2.
D
give me Je - sus on the line. Op - er - line. Please give me
give me Je - sus on the
G
D
(F♯ Bass)
Em7
G
(A Bass)
D
G
D
(F♯ Bass)
Em7
G
(A Bass)
Je - sus on the line. Please give me Je - sus on the
rit.
G
D
line, yeah, yeah, yeah, yeah.

TODAY

Recorded by JOHN DENVER on RCA Records

Words and Music by
RANDY SPARKS

Moderately slow

Chorus
To-day while the blos-soms still cling to the vine, I'll taste your straw-ber-ries, I'll drink your sweet wine. A mil-lion to-mor-rows shall all pass a-way, Ere I for-get all the joy that is mine, To-day.

Copyright © 1964 METRO-GOLDWYN-MAYER, INC., Culver City, California
Rights throughout the world controlled by MILLER MUSIC CORPORATION, New York, N.Y.
By arrangement with HERITAGE HOUSE
International Copyright Secured   Made in U.S.A.   All Rights Reserved

Verse

(1.) I'll be a dandy and I'll be a rover, You'll know who I am by the song that I sing. I'll feast at your table, I'll sleep in your clover, Who cares what the morrow shall bring. To-

(2.) can't be contented with yesterday's glory, I can't live on promises winter to spring. Today is my moment and now is my story, I'll laugh, and I'll cry, and I'll sing.

MOONLIGHT SERENADE

Recorded by BOBBY VINTON on ABC Records

Lyric by
MITCHELL PARISH

Music by
GLENN MILLER

Moderately

I stand at your gate and the song that I sing is of moon-light, I stand and I wait for the touch of your hand in the June night, The ros-es are sigh-ing a Moon-light Ser-e-nade. The

stars are a-glow and to-night how their light sets me dream-ing, My love, and do you know that your eyes are like stars bright-ly beam-ing? I bring you and sing you a Moon-light Ser-e-nade.

Copyright © 1939 (Renewed 1967) ROBBINS MUSIC CORPORATION, New York, N.Y.
International Copyright Secured   Made in U.S.A.   All Rights Reserved

B♭maj7 B♭m6 Em7 A7 Cm6 D7+5
Let us stray till break of day in love's val - ley of dreams, Just
mf
Dm6 E7 Dm6 E7 Cm6 D7 Gm7 C7-9
you and I, a sum-mer sky, a heav - en - ly breeze kiss - ing the trees. So
mp
F6 A♭dim Gm7 Cdim C7 C7+5
don't let me wait, come to me ten - der - ly in the June night, I
F Fmaj7 F7 D7 Gm
stand at your gate and I sing you a song in the moon - light, A
F Edim F Gm Gdim Gm C7 C7+5 F F6
love song, my dar - ling, a Moon - light Ser - e - nade.
rit. e dim.

EV'RY DAY OF MY LIFE

Recorded by BOBBY VINTON on EPIC Records

Words and Music by
JIMMIE CRANE
AL JACOBS

Moderately with feeling

EV-'RY DAY OF MY LIFE _____ I'll be in love with you,

EV-'RY DAY OF MY LIFE _____ I prom-ise I'll be true.

I'll nev-er make you cry, _____ And as the years go by _____

I'll al-ways try to do _____ what pleas-es you. _____

Copyright © 1953, 1954 MILLER MUSIC CORPORATION, New York, N.Y.
International Copyright Secured   Made in U.S.A.   All Rights Reserved

EV-'RY DAY OF MY LIFE_____ I'll need you close to me,____
And if I have my way_____ that's where you'll always be____
I'll prove how much I love you over and over a-
gain, Ev-'ry mo-ment I live,_____ EV-'RY DAY OF MY
LIFE. EV-'RY DAY OF MY LIFE.____

Recorded by HENRY GROSS on LIFESONG Records

SHANNON

Words and Music by
HENRY GROSS

Moderately slow

An-oth-er day is at end, Ma-ma says she's tired a-gain, No one can e-ven be-gin to tell her. I hard-ly know what to say, but maybe it's better that way,

If papa were here I'm sure he'd tell her.

Shannon is gone, I hope she's drifting out to sea,

She always loved to swim away.

Csus4
C
F
Gm
F
May-be she'll find an is-land with a shad-y tree,
Eb (Bb bass)
Bb
F
Eb
Bb
Dm7
Just like the one in our back-yard.
G9
To Coda
F
Gm7
C
3
Ma-ma tries hard to pre-tend things will get
mf
Fsus4
F
F (E bass)
Dm
Dm (C bass)
Dm (B bass)
A
bet-ter a-gain, Some-how she's keep-ing it all in-side

her. But fi-n'lly the tears fill our eyes and I know that some-where to-night She knows how much we real-ly miss her.

Just like the one in our back-yard.

D. S. al Coda

Coda

rit.

I'M EASY

From The Motion Picture "NASHVILLE"
ACADEMY AWARD WINNER
Recorded by KEITH CARRADINE on ABC Records

Words and Music by
KEITH CARRADINE

Moderato (with feeling)

It's not my way to love you just when no-one's look-ing. It's not my way to take your hand if I'm not sure. It's not my way to let you see what's go-ing on in-side of me; when it's a love you won't be need-ing, you're not free. Please stop

pull-ing at my sleeve if you're just play-ing, if you won't
on if there's no-where for you to take me, if lov-ing
fav-ors, let me watch you from a dis-tance, 'cause when you're

take the things you make me want to give. I nev-er cared too much for games and this one's
you would have me be a some-time thing. I can't put bars on my in-sides; my love is
near, I find it hard to keep my head. And when your eyes throw light at mine, it's e-

driv-ing me in-sane; you're not half as free to wan-der as you claim.
some-thing I can't hide; it still hurts when I re-call the times I tried.
nough to change my mind, make me leave my cau-tious words and ways be-hind.

1.2.
G
C
Dm
But, I'm eas - y. Yeah, I'm eas - y. Give the
But, I'm eas - y. Yeah, I'm eas - y. Take my
Em
Fmaj7
word, I'll play the game as though that's how it ought to be, be-cause I'm eas -
hand and pull me down, I won't put up an - y fight, be-cause I'm eas -
Cmaj7
y.
y.
2. Don't lead me
3. Don't do me
3.
G
Cmaj7
Dm
That's why I'm eas - y, yeah, I'm eas - y. Say you

Em
Fmaj7
want me, I'll come run - ning with-out tak - ing time to think, 'cause I'm eas-
Cmaj7
Dm
Em
y. Yeah, I'm eas - y. Take my hand and pull me down. I
F
Cmaj7
Dm
won't put up an-y fight, be-cause I'm eas - y. Yeah, I'm eas - y. Give the
Em
Fmaj7
Cmaj7
word, I'll play your game as though that's how it ought to be, be-cause I'm eas - y.

DO YOU BELIEVE IN MAGIC

Recorded by THE LOVIN' SPOONFUL on KAMA SUTRA Records

Words and Music by JOHN B. SEBASTIAN

Moderately

1. Do you be-lieve in mag-ic in a young girl's heart How the mu-sic can free her when-ev-er it starts And it's mag-ic if the mu-sic is groov-y it makes you feel hap-py like an old time mov-ie I'll tell you 'bout the mag-ic and a free your soul But it's like try-in' to tell a stran-ger 'bout a rock and roll.

2. If you be-lieve in mag-ic don't both-er to choose, If it's jug band mu-sic or

3. (If you be-lieve in mag)-ic come a-long with me We'll dance un-til morn-ing 'til there's

Copyright © 1965 THE HUDSON BAY MUSIC COMPANY, 1619 Broadway, New York, N.Y. 10019
International Copyright Secured — Made in U.S.A. — All Rights Reserved
Used by permission

rhy-thm and blues, Just go and lis-ten, it-'ll start with a smile that won't wipe off your face no mat-ter how hard you try. Your feet start tap-pin' and you can't seem to find How you got there so just blow your mind.

just you and me And may-be if the mu-sic is right I'll meet you to-mor-row sort of late at night. And we'll go danc-in' ba-by then you'll see How the

3. If you be-lieve in mag- mag-ic's in the mu-sic and the mu-sic's in me. Yeah! Do

Fade till finish

you be-lieve like I be-lieve? Do you be-lieve like I be-lieve? Do

ONE PIECE AT A TIME

Recorded by JOHNNY CASH on COLUMBIA Records

Words and Music by
WAYNE KEMP

Talking Blues tempo

1. Well, I left Kentucky back in forty-nine and went to Detroit workin' on assembly lines. The first year, they had me puttin' wheels on Cadillacs. Ev'ry day, I'd watch them beauties roll by, and sometimes I'd hang my head and cry. 'Cause I

Copyright © 1976 by TREE PUBLISHING CO., INC., 8 Music Square West, Nashville, Tennessee 37203
International Copyright Secured   Made in U.S.A.
Used by permission   All Rights Reserved

al-ways want-ed me one that was long and black. 2. One day I de-vised my-self a plan that should be the en-vy of 'most an-y man. I'd sneak it out-ta there in a lunch box in my hand. Now, get-tin' caught meant get-tin' fired, But I fig-ured I'd have it all by the time I re-tired. I'd

236

have me a car worth at least a hun-dred grand.

Chorus
I'd get it one piece at a time, And it would-n't cost me a dime. You'd know it's me when I come through your town. I'm gon-na ride a-round in style; I'm gon-na drive ev-'ry-bod-y

2650

wild. 'Cause I'll have the on - ly one there is a - round.

RECITATION

3. So, the very next day when I punched in with my big lunch box
   And with help from my friends, I left that day with a lunch box full of gears.
   I've never considered myself a thief, but GM wouldn't miss just one little piece
   Especially if I strung it out over several years.

4. The first day, I got me a fuel pump, and the next day I got me an engine and a trunk.
   Then, I got me a transmission and all the chrome.
   The little things I could get in the big lunch box
   Like nuts and bolts and all four shocks.
   But the big stuff we snuck out in my buddy's mobile home.

5. Now, up to now, my plan went all right, 'til we tried to put it all together one night.
   And that's when we noticed that something was definitely wrong.
   The transmission was a '53, and the motor turned out to be a '73,
   And when we tried to put in the bolts, all the holes were gone.
   So, we drilled it out so that it would fit, and with a little bit of help from an adapter kit,
   We had that engine running just like a song.

6. Now the headlights, they was another sight,
   We had two on the left, and one on the right.
   But when we pulled out the switch, all three of 'em come on.
   The back end looked kinda funny, too.
   But we put it together, and when we got through, well, that's when we noticed that we only had one tail fin.
   About that time, my wife walked out, and I could see in her eyes that she had her doubts.
   But she opened the door and said, "Honey, take me for a spin."

7. So, we drove uptown just to get the tags, and I headed her right on down the main drag.
   I could hear everybody laughin' for blocks around.
   But, up there at the court house, they didn't laugh,
   'Cause to type it up, it took the whole staff.
   And when they got through, the title weighed sixty pounds.

2nd CHORUS: I got it one piece at a time, and it didn't cost me a dime.
             You'll know it's me when I come through your town.
             I'm gonna ride around in style; I'm gonna drive everybody wild,
             'Cause I'll have the only one there is around.

(Ad lib):   "Yeah, Red Rider, this is the Cottonmouth in the Psychobilly Cadillac, com'on? This
             is the Cotton-mouth, a negatory on the cost of this mo-chine, there, Red Rider, you might
             say I went right up to the factory and picked it up, it's cheaper that way. What model is
             it? ..... Well, it's a 49, 50, 51, 52, 53, 54, 55, 56, 57, 58, 59 automobile... 60, 61,
             62, 63, 64, 65, 66, 67, 68, 69 automobile .... 70, 71, 72, 73 ....."

(They Long To Be) CLOSE TO YOU

Words by HAL DAVID
Music by BURT BACHARACH

Slowly and Steady

Why do birds sud-den-ly ap-pear ev-'ry- time you are near. Just like me, THEY LONG TO BE CLOSE TO YOU.

Why do stars fall down from the sky ev-'ry- time you walk by. Just like me, THEY LONG TO BE CLOSE TO YOU.

Copyright © 1963, 1969 by U.S. SONGS, INC., BLUE SEAS MUSIC, INC. and JAC MUSIC CO., INC.
International Copyright Secured   Made in U.S.A.   All Rights Reserved
Used by permission

Eb6 Eb7 Ab 4 fr.
On the day that you were born the an- gels got to- geth- er and de-
mf
Gm C9sus4 C9 C7 Ab 4 fr.
cid- ed to cre-ate a dream come true. So they sprin- kled moon dust in your hair of
f
Abmaj7 Ab6 Bb
Tacet
8va Loco
gold and star-light in your eyes of blue. That is
mp
Ab 4 fr. G7sus4 G7 Gm7 Cm7
why all the boys in town fol-low you all a- round.
mf
Keep Repeating and Fade Out
Ab 4 fr. Eb6 Ebmaj7 Eb6 Ebmaj7
Just like me, THEY LONG TO BE CLOSE TO YOU.
dim. poco a poco

I LOVE MUSIC (Part 1)

Recorded by THE O'JAYS on PHILADELPHIA INTERNATIONAL Records

Words and Music by
KENNY GAMBLE
LEON HUFF

I love music,
I love music,
an-y kind o' music,
sweet, sweet mu-sic,
I love mu-sic
long as it's swing-ing,
just as long
all the joy
as it's groov-in'.
that it's bring-ing.
Makes me laugh, makes me smile all the
I'm so hap-py to be in com-

Copyright © 1975 MIGHTY THREE MUSIC
All rights administered by BLACKWOOD MUSIC INC., 51 West 52nd Street, New York, N.Y.
International Copyright Secured   Made in U.S.A.   All Rights Reserved
Used by permission

while when-ev-er I'm with you, girl. While we dance, make ro-mance, I'm en-
plete har-mo-ny, I love you, girl. As I hold you so close in my

chant-ed by the things that you do.
arms, I'm so glad that you're mine.

Noth-in' can be bet-ter than a sweet love song

when you got the girl that you love in your arms.

Mu-sic is the heal-ing force of the world, it's under-

stood by ev-'ry man, wom-an, boy an' girl.

I love mu-sic, an-y kind o' mu-sic,

I love mu-sic, just as long as it's groov-in'.

Mu-sic makes the at-mos-phere so fine, es-pe-cially when you got a cold glass of wine.

Repeat and fade

I love, I love, I love, I love, I love mu-sic.

Recorded by THE CARPENTERS on A&M Records

Words by
PAUL WILLIAMS

WE'VE ONLY JUST BEGUN

Music by
ROGER NICHOLS

new to us, Watch-ing the signs a-long the way, Talk-ing it o-ver just the two of us, Work-ing to-geth-er day to day to-geth-er.

D.S. al Coda

We've On-ly Just Be-gun.

Fade out ....

THEY JUST CAN'T STOP IT
(The Games People Play)

Recorded by THE SPINNERS on ATLANTIC Records

Words and Music by
CHARLES SIMMONS
BRUCE HAWES
JOSEPH B. JEFFERSON

Verse:

Can't get no rest,___ don't know how I'll work all day,___
spent all that day___ fix-in' up to go some-where,___
Twelve-for-ty-five,___ head-ed for the sub-way home,___

When will I learn___ mem-o-ries get in the way.___
Thought I was late___ and I found she was-n't there.___
I took my time___ 'cause I felt so all a-lone.___

I walk a-round,___ I can't hear a sound, folks talk-in' loud,
I guess I'll find___ love peace o' mind some oth-er time,
Not far a-way___ I heard a fun-ny sound, took a look a-round,

Copyright © 1974, 1975 MIGHTY THREE MUSIC
All rights administered by BLACKWOOD MUSIC INC., 51 West 52nd Street, New York, N.Y.
International Copyright Secured   Made in U.S.A.   All Rights Reserved
Used by permission

But I don't see at all, I gotta get a-way, gotta get a-way. I don't know where to go, It's hope-less so I guess I'll leave it a-lone.

But I still have to-day, I gotta get a-way, gotta get a-way. I don't know where to go, It's hope-less so I guess I'll

And I could see her face smile as she came, call-in' out my name. So I know where to go, We'll take it slow, I guess I'll

Well, I leave it a-lone.
call it a day.

Chorus:
Games peo-ple play,___ night or day they're just not match-in'.
What they should do___ keeps me feel-in' blue.

D7 Gmaj7 Bm7 Am7
Been down too long, right, wrong, I
D7 Gmaj7 Bm7
To Coda
just can't stop it. Spend - in' all day think - in' just of you.
Esus4 E7 Esus4 E7
D.C. al Coda
Coda
Am7 D11
D.S. (Chorus) and fade
D7
think - in' just of you.

Recorded by GEORGE BENSON on WARNER BROS. Records

BREEZIN'

By
BOBBY WOMACK

Moderate Bossa Nova

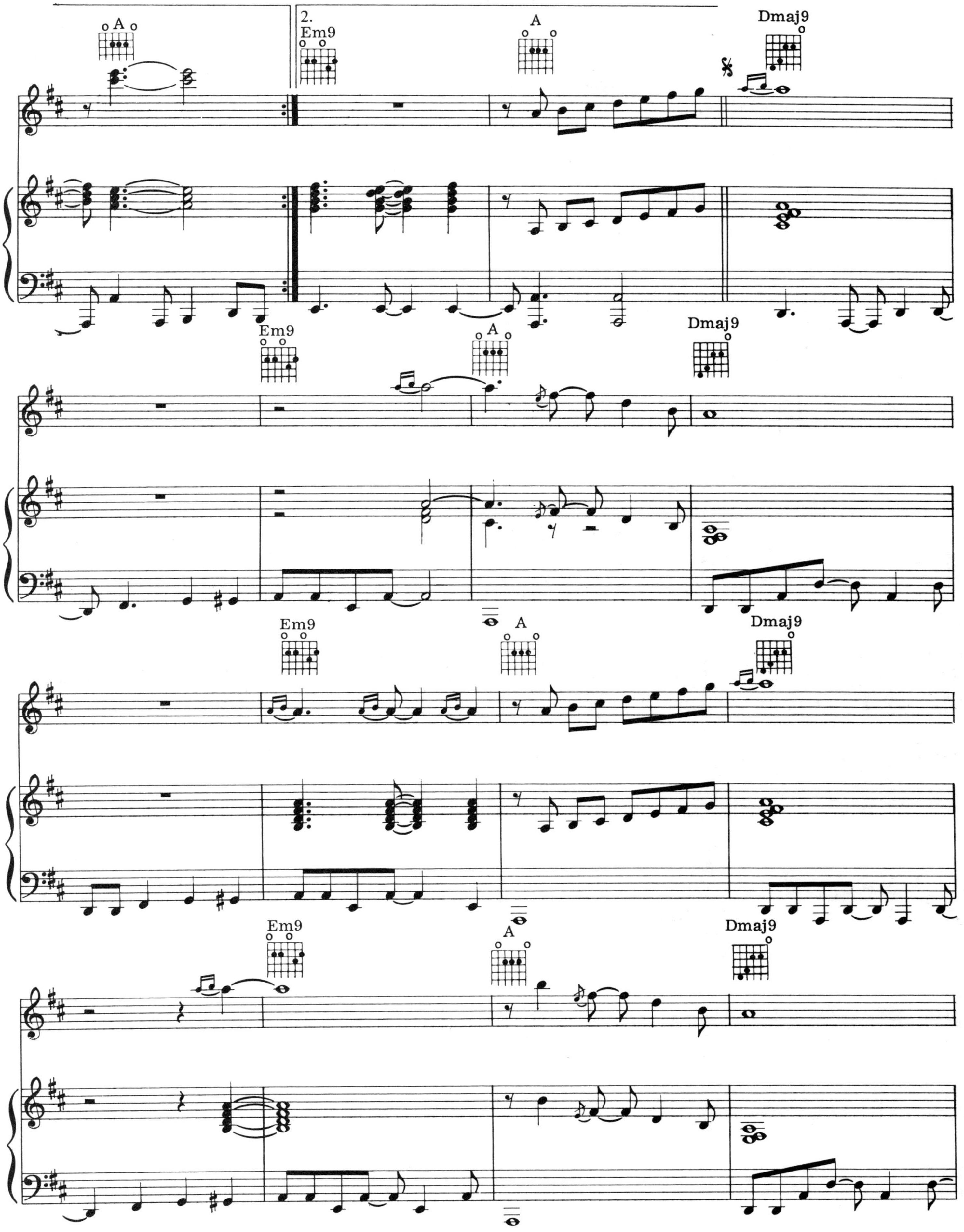
A
2.
Em9
A
Dmaj9
Em9
A
Dmaj9
Em9
A
Dmaj9
Em9
A
Dmaj9

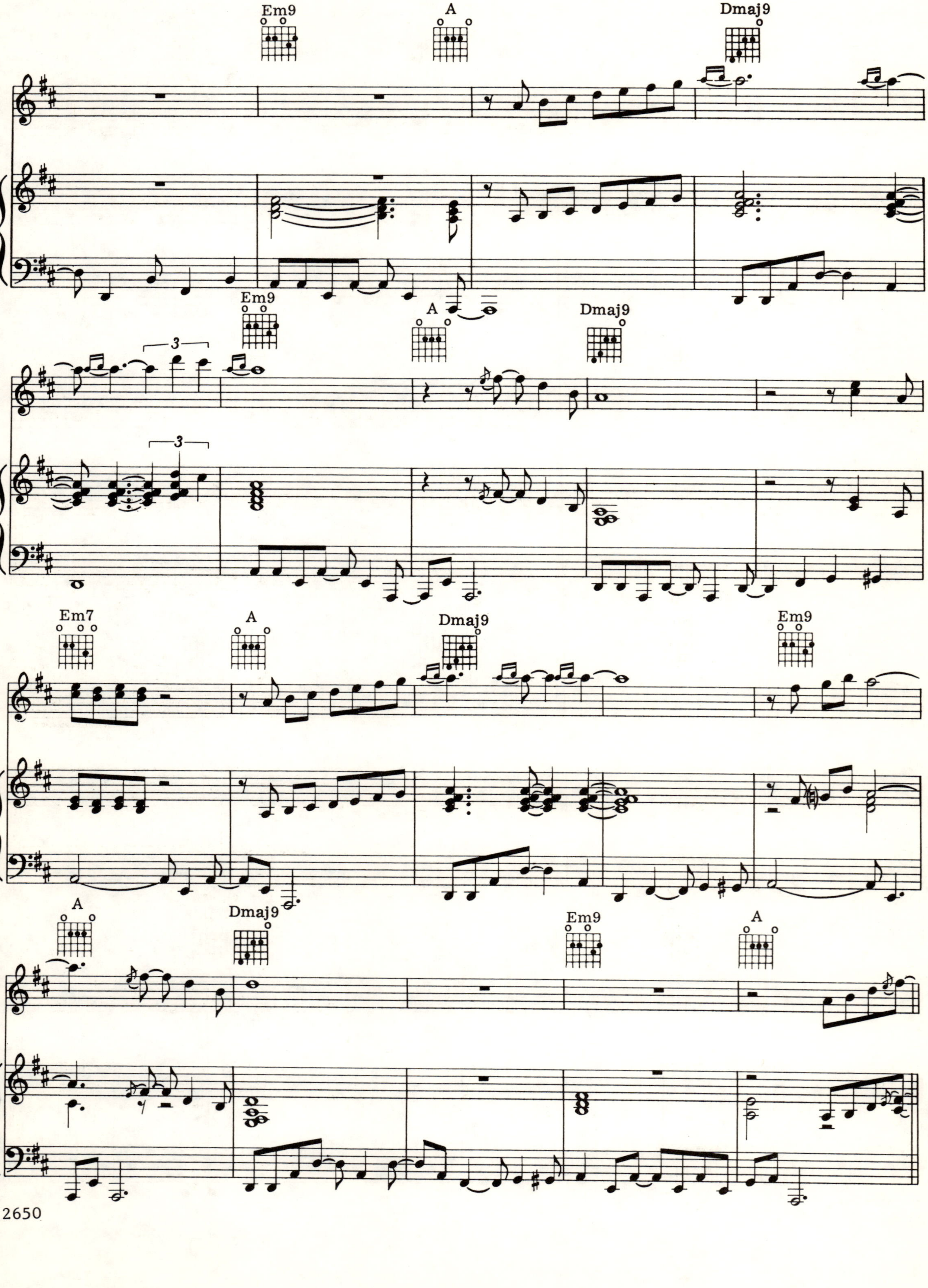
Em9
A
Dmaj9
Em9
A
Dmaj9
3
3
Em7
A
Dmaj9
Em9
A
Dmaj9
Em9
A

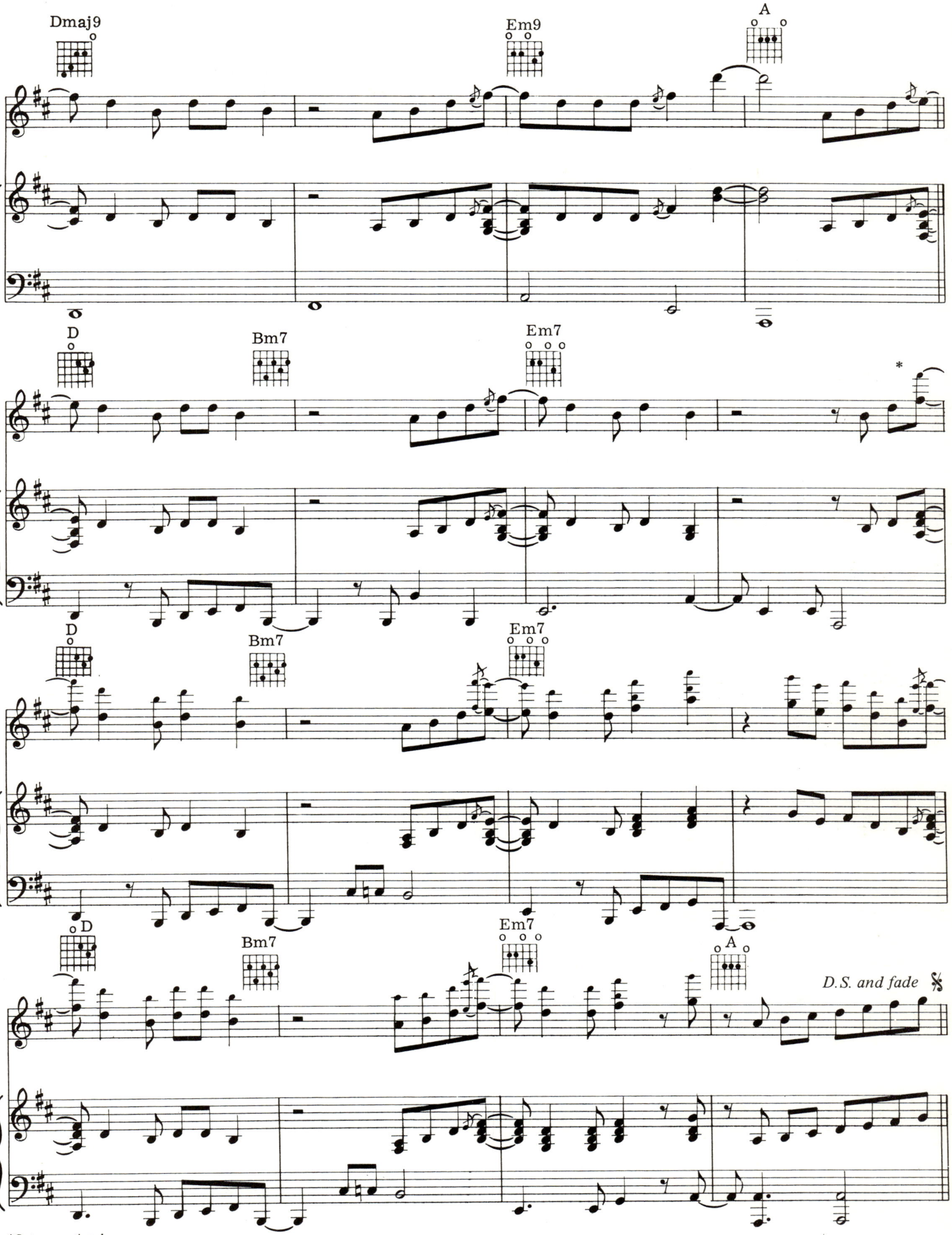

*Octaves optional

LEAVE ME ALONE
(Ruby Red Dress)

Recorded by HELEN REDDY on CAPITOL Records

Words and Music by
LINDA LAURIE

Moderately with a beat

Big ole Ruby Red Dress wanders 'round the town Talk-in' to her-self
Big ole Ruby Red Dress ev-'ry-bod-y laughs Say she's got no fu-

now, some-times set-tin' down. Don't you get too close now,
ture, and nev-er made no past. Some-thing hurt that Ru-by,

Ru-by runs a-way. Poor ole Ru-by Red Dress, born on a sor-ry day.
some-thing she can't bear. Ya look at her real close now ya see a lit-tle tear.

Copyright © 1973 by ANNE-RACHEL MUSIC CORPORATION and THE BROOKLYN MUSIC COMPANY
The rights of ANNE-RACHEL MUSIC CORPORATION assigned to CHAPPELL & CO., INC.
All rights administered by CHAPPELL & CO., INC., New York, N.Y.
International Copyright Secured   ALL RIGHTS RESERVED including public performance for profit   Made in U.S.A.
Any copying, arranging or adapting of this composition without the consent of the owner is an infringement of copyright
Used by permission

I can hear her say
When she says now } Leave me a-lone,— won't you leave me a-lone,— Please leave me a-lone— now leave me a-lone.— Leave me a-lone— please leave me a-lone— yes, leave me.

Last time fade

Leave me a-lone,— won't you leave me a-lone,— Please leave me a-lone— now leave me a-lone.— Leave me a-lone— just leave me a-lone— oh leave me.

Some folks say some farm boy up from Tennessee

Taught it all to Ruby then just let her be.

Her daddy tried to hide it, tried to keep things cool.

But something happened to Ruby, she broke down to a fool. Who just says now

D. S. to fade